THE ROTHAMSTED MONOGRAPHS ON
AGRICULTURAL SCIENCE

EDITED BY
Sir E. JOHN RUSSELL, D.Sc., F.R.S.

PROBLEMS IN SOIL MICROBIOLOGY

PROBLEMS IN
SOIL MICROBIOLOGY

BY

D. WARD CUTLER

GENERAL MICROBIOLOGY DEPARTMENT
ROTHAMSTED EXPERIMENTAL STATION
HARPENDEN

AND

LETTICE M. CRUMP

GENERAL MICROBIOLOGY DEPARTMENT
ROTHAMSTED EXPERIMENTAL STATION
HARPENDEN

*WITH DIAGRAMS
AND A MAP*

LONGMANS, GREEN AND CO.
LONDON ◆ NEW YORK ◆ TORONTO

LONGMANS, GREEN AND CO. LTD.
39 PATERNOSTER ROW, LONDON, E.C. 4
6 OLD COURT HOUSE STREET, CALCUTTA
53 NICOL ROAD, BOMBAY
36A MOUNT ROAD, MADRAS

LONGMANS, GREEN AND CO.
114 FIFTH AVENUE, NEW YORK
221 EAST 20TH STREET, CHICAGO
88 TREMONT STREET, BOSTON

LONGMANS, GREEN AND CO.
480 UNIVERSITY AVENUE, TORONTO

FIRST PUBLISHED . . JULY 1935

Printed in Great Britain

PREFACE.

THIS book incorporates the substance of a series of lectures delivered by one of us (D. W. C.) at the University College of Wales, Aberystwyth, on the Aberystwyth Lectures Foundation during the session 1934-35. The contents are largely the result of work carried out in the General Microbiology Department of the Rothamsted Experimental Station by the authors and their colleagues, and it is in no sense a textbook of soil microbiology.

The theme throughout is to show that from the biologist's viewpoint the soil is an eminently suitable home for living organisms and that, through the long ages of evolution, a population has been selected which is, on the whole, so unspecialised that almost any substance which finds its way into the soil, either naturally or in the course of modern agricultural practice, will eventually become incorporated into the general soil economy. The activities of each micro-organism depend upon those of its fellows, and the threads of all their lives together form a skein which is still inextricably tangled ; the whole problem can only be attacked by tracing the threads one by one, and the results of some of these attempts at disentangling the threads are given in this book.

Our thanks are due to those of our colleagues who have so helpfully discussed with us some of the chemical and physical aspects of our problems, and in fairness to them we leave them nameless since we may have misinterpreted their views.

We are also greatly indebted to our colleagues, both past and present, of the General Microbiology Department who have helped in our experimental work, and to Miss Mabel Dunkley for her care in the preparation of the Tables and Manuscript. To Messrs. Sidgwick & Jackson our thanks are due for permission to quote from Mr. Elton's book, *Animal Ecology*.

D. WARD CUTLER.
LETTICE M. CRUMP.

GENERAL MICROBIOLOGY DEPARTMENT,
ROTHAMSTED EXPERIMENTAL STATION,
HARPENDEN, *February, 1935.*

CONTENTS.

CHAPTER I.

Since prehistoric man first settled down from his nomadic existence and learnt the arts of cultivating the ground and planting it with crops, which he could domesticate for his own use, soil has been handled by countless generations of husbandmen whose business and pleasure it has been to make it yield to its uttermost capacity. Yet the study of the actual structure of the soil is still a young science, and even now the story is incomplete.

The old idea of the soil as a collection of solid mineral particles forming a more or less compact mass, with air circulating in the spaces, and with the water forming a thin film around each granule, has been overthrown by modern work on the colloidal structure of clay and by the resulting conception of the majority of soil particles as composite structures. At the present time it is very difficult to get a clear picture of the soil structure, however, because adequate methods of research have not yet been discovered, and so different workers can erect diverse theoretical super-structures on a basis of the same facts ; nevertheless, it is worth while before considering the micro-organisms of the soil, and their actions and interactions, to try to outline what may be regarded as their normal abode, even though the picture given may need to be redrawn as the soil physicist's knowledge increases.

A well-manured soil in good tilth consists of mineral particles of very different shapes and sizes, together with

I

organic matter, gases, and water which usually contains various salts in solution.   In the formation of soil from the original rock the first stage is the production of progressively smaller mineral particles by the action of agencies such as frost ;   meanwhile, rain water containing carbon dioxide and other dissolved substances percolates among the particles, and gradually brings about chemical changes which lead to actual change and decomposition of the mineral matter.   Particles of all sizes are also constantly transferred from one place to another by wind and by water, so that in the course of time they may reappear in localities very remote from the place of their origin.   These processes have been going on during the geological ages and are still in operation, rocks are still crumbling, and their particles are still being disintegrated, and carried from place to place or are settling down into the soil in the neighbourhood of the parent structure.   The gravel, sand, and silt fractions of the soil have been formed by disintegration of the original materials, while the clay fraction is a product of actual chemical decomposition ;   all these may differ in composition in various soils according to the nature of the original rock from which they were formed, though these differences may subsequently disappear under the influence of similar climatic conditions. From the agriculturist's point of view all particles below 0·002 millimetres in diameter are classified as clay, while the other fractions are arranged as shown in Table 1.

But the mineral part of the soil must not be considered

TABLE 1.—FRACTIONS OBTAINED BY MECHANICAL ANALYSIS OF SOILS.
(BRITISH AND INTERNATIONAL.)

Fraction.	Limits of Diameter of Particles in Mm.
Gravel .	above 2
Coarse sand .	2·0-0·2
Fine sand .	0·2-0·02
Silt .	0·02-0·002
Clay .	below 0·002

as a mere mass of particles which are perpetually becoming smaller and smaller, for the clay possesses the power of binding the individual mineral fragments that constitute the soil into crumbs which often possess typical shapes and sizes. A crumb may therefore be looked upon as an aggregation of particles held together by the colloidal material to form a larger mass, which, in many respects, behaves as a structural unit. From the method of construction it follows that such crumbs contain small spaces, many of them of only capillary size, which are conveniently known as the micro-pores, while the pores between the crumbs themselves may be called the macro-pores ; all the spaces in the soil either between the crumbs, or incorporated within the crumb structure itself, allow of the presence of air and of water, and also of gaseous and liquid circulation. The great majority of organisms require free oxygen for their respiration, and in the larger spaces or macro-pores there will undoubtedly be enough to satisfy all normal requirements, since their contents are constantly renewed from the air above the surface of the ground by the action of various agencies and also by changes in the level of the water table. In actual practice it has been found that this soil air in the majority of cases contains only a slightly higher percentage of carbon dioxide than does the ordinary atmosphere (38). In soils in which the water content is abnormally high, or during periods when the air circulation is restricted, the supply of oxygen even in the macro-pore spaces may become extremely low.

Normally the soil air is renewed and kept in movement by a variety of factors of which probably the change in temperature between night and day is the chief. The nightly fall in temperature is accompanied by contraction of the air which is already present in the soil pores, and this leads to fresh air being drawn in from above the surface to fill the spaces; the daily rise in temperature naturally has the reverse effect and the soil breathes out some of its gases into the atmosphere. In addition to this, wind passing over the surface of the soil has a ventilating action, while gaseous diffusion also plays a small part. The ventilation of the soil is conditioned by two factors, the amount of air present and the rate at which it is renewed. Given a spell of cold, dry weather a relatively high proportion of air may be present, but very little will pass in and out of the soil, while in the event of the soil becoming water-logged there will naturally be very little air present, but what there is may be rapidly changed, provided that it is not enclosed in pockets by the water. All conditions from practically normal air to complete anaerobicity can be met with, though a real dearth of oxygen is probably only a temporary state of affairs and confined to certain localised areas ; but nevertheless it probably occurs sufficiently often to give organisms which can withstand temporary anaerobic conditions a better chance of survival than those which are obligate aerobes.

The soil solution like the soil air is distributed between the micro and macro-pore spaces, and is affected by a variety of factors. Among these rainfall is obviously one of the most important, but there are also factors which may increase or decrease the rate of evaporation such as changes in the wind and the temperature, while the height of the water table, plant growth, and cultivation also influence the amount of soil water ; any or all of these, although they constantly cause local changes both in the composition and the concentration of the solution, at the same time tend to maintain a certain homogeneity and to prevent stagnation by encouraging movement. This movement may often be considerable, and is for the most part of a slow and steady nature, but, owing to the capillary structure of the soil, sudden changes in surface tension may be induced which cause small though violent currents to occur.

The water in the soil presents a very intricate problem ; the colloidal clay is responsible for holding a certain amount so firmly that it is not available for the needs of living things and so plays no part in the life that goes on in the soil. Apart from this held water, any liquid which is present must, as has been seen, lie either in the capillary spaces and pockets within the crumbs, or in the spaces between the crumbs and any other solid materials that the soil may contain, and in all probability it is always a nutrient solution containing mineral salts and organic matter. This forms an ideal medium for the life and reproduction of the micro-organisms, and, even under conditions of exceptional dryness, enough is always present within the crumbs themselves to support a permanent population. When there is so much liquid present that it invades the inter crumb spaces minute isolated lakes will be formed which are much more temporary. These will never fill the spaces except in a water-logged soil, but will normally run into the capillary spaces between particles and spread out round the solid surfaces in a thin film which is constantly held under tension, and presents a large area for aeration in proportion to its volume. Inside the crumbs, where the spaces may range in size from the smallest capillaries to comparatively large pockets, from the point of view of aeration and of circulation and composition of the soil solution each will be a law unto itself. The smaller capillaries will undoubtedly as a rule be full of water, and, if as must sometimes happen, they form the sole connection between the macro-pore spaces and the air pockets within the crumb, these latter will often be sealed off temporarily and anaerobic conditions may ensue for short periods ; when, on the other hand, the spaces in the crumb are in free communication with those outside it conditions will be approximately the same in both of them. Since it is the same spaces that contain the air and water any decrease in the volume of one will usually be reflected in an increase in the other, and in this way heavy rain may considerably reduce the amount of air in the soil. From the point of view of the organisms all changes, which keep the gases and the soil solution in a continual state of movement, have the important effect of ensuring the renewal of the medium and preventing the accumulation of excretory products, while they also tend to keep a certain standard of homogeneity of the habitat.

The organisms which make their permanent home in the superficial layers of the earth's crust fall into two groups, which, though their biological requirements may be the same, are very different from the point of view of their mode of life. The larger forms, which include the various species of earthworms and a very large number and variety of insects, are independent of the crumb structure of the soil, since they live in the spaces between the crumbs and make their way through the earth by constant displacement of the obstacles in their way. The insects are without effect upon the crumbs themselves, as they merely change the relative positions and thereby alter the shape and volume of the spaces, but the worms, apart from this, also actually swallow a high percentage of the material that they encounter in their passage. The importance of these larger animals is considerable; it is only necessary to remember Darwin's calculation that, in an acre of land containing an average number of earthworms, as much as 10 tons of dry soil may pass through their bodies annually, to realize the part which they must play in keeping the soil in motion. Further, the amount of finely divided soil which they bring to the surface may form a layer of more than a tenth of an inch in thickness every year.

The microscopic forms, on the other hand, such as the bacteria and protozoa, cannot live actively except in a film of liquid, and hence are confined to the surface of particles or to the spaces within the crumbs. For these microorganisms the crumb provides a stronghold, where there is adequate moisture except under very abnormal conditions of drought, and where, although the ventilation may be faulty, an adaptable organism will only experience temporary inconvenience.

It must always be borne in mind that if any particular habitat is to be colonised by plants or animals it must fulfil certain conditions which are essential for life. Adequate supplies of food and water and the removal of waste products are always necessary, and the presence of oxygen is required in the great majority of cases, while the range of both the temperature and of the reaction of the medium must not be too extreme nor subject to very sudden changes. This last requirement would appear to be the more important, as both protozoa and bacteria can live at very great extremes of pH value, provided that they are brought to them by slow gradations. It has already been seen that in soil, provided it is in a condition which allows of the circulation of gases and liquids, there are adequate amounts of both oxygen and water, and, moreover, in such soil there is no likelihood of waste products accumulating.

The micro-population is composed of many different kinds of organisms, whose food requirements are very different, but ultimately they all depend on the amount of decomposable organic matter that is present. This forms the food supply of bacteria and fungi, which in their turn feed the protozoa, while the soluble by-products which are produced by bacterial action provide food for the green plants. Soils which are deficient in organic matter obviously cannot maintain so large a population as those in which the organic matter is plentiful. But the decomposition of the organic matter depends not only on the presence of suitable organisms, but also on an adequate supply of other food substances; for instance, the ratio of nitrogen to carbon undoubtedly affects bacterial activity, and bacteria are as dependent as are green plants on a medium supplying the other elements that are necessary for growth. The various soil processes, such as ammonification, nitrification, and carbohydrate decomposition, are the results of the action of many different kinds of bacteria, and so far little is known as to the affect upon these chemical activities of the interaction of the various species and the changes in the environment.

The presence of protozoa further complicates the issue ; the majority of those in soil feed on bacteria ; but whether they select among the species of bacteria or devour any that they come across is not definitely known, but as will be seen later there is considerable evidence showing that selective feeding occurs.

Turning to the question of the constancy of the temperature and of the reaction of the environment it is found that within the soil the temperature changes from day to day are always very much less than those which are experienced in the air, and the range of temperatures is more restricted. On a hot day in August when the air temperature ranged from 57·0°-88·3° Fahrenheit the temperature in the soil at 8 inches below the surface rose from 69·0° at nine o'clock in the morning to 77·0° twelve hours later, a change of only 8° in the soil as against 31° in the air. In winter the same thing is seen, for on a cold December day, when the air temperature ranged from 22·8°-33·0°, the soil temperature remained constant at 32·2°.

The reactions of soils, as measured by the hydrogen ion concentration, show a very wide range, the extremes recorded being 2·8 on the one hand and 9·7 on the other (37). These are, of course, exceptional, but in English arable soils, such as occur on the Rothamsted farm, there is a range of from 5·7 on a plot receiving ammonium sulphate and rape cake to 8·2 on one which had been previously limed. For the most part soils are very well buffered, with the result that the reaction changes very slowly, if at all, from year to year under natural conditions ; and even when a change is induced by the application of artificial manures it occurs comparatively slowly. It is in the case of soils that are not strongly buffered, such as light sandy ones, that the application of acid-producing artificials may cause rapid changes in the acidity.

From the point of view then of the living organism a soil in good tilth must be regarded as offering an ideal environment; the crumb provides a nidus for both bacteria and protozoa, where they are always sure of adequate food and moisture, while the oxygen supply, too, is usually satisfactory. Conditions of temporary anaerobicity, however, which are enough to kill the active forms of the majority of the protozoa, will not eliminate the species, since there is always a proportion which are passing through the encysted stage of their life cycle, and in this state they are unaffected by adverse external conditions to a great extent. Among the bacteria there are also species which form similar resistant spores, and even apart from this an ability to adapt themselves to a scarcity of oxygen is a common faculty among the soil forms. The absence of sudden or extreme variations in its physical condition help to make the soil a safe home, since most organisms are intolerant of gross changes, but can adapt themselves to gradual ones.

For reasons such as these it is not surprising that the soil has a very large and diverse population which it maintains day after day and year after year, regardless of changing circumstances in the world above ; and it is to this population that the soil owes its unique power of acting as a universal scavenger. There are very few things that cannot in time be incorporated into its structure and used for plant or animal food, or for building up the soil crumbs which form the firm foundation of the whole material world.

CHAPTER II.

FOR many years it has been known that the soil harbours large numbers of bacteria and various methods have been devised for counting them. The methods usually employed have been indirect, and have been based upon the making of a series of dilutions from a suspension of a known quantity of soil, and samples from each dilution are then plated out on some form of solid nutrient medium. In such media it is assumed that each colony that develops is produced from a single bacterium and so, by calculation, the numbers per gramme of soil can be deduced.

This method suffers from the disadvantages that its accuracy depends on all the bacteria being evenly dispersed as single cells through the diluting solutions, and on every individual being able to grow to form a colony on one and the same medium. Since it is improbable that these conditions are ever completely fulfilled, it follows that a plate count will always tend to give a lower number than is actually present. Attempts to observe the soil inhabitants directly under the microscope by crushing soil in water are very unsatisfactory, for it is rare to be able to see any bacteria by such means even when many hundreds are known to be present. This is partly owing to the opacity of the soil particles which make blind spots in which nothing can be detected, but still more to the tenacity with which the micro-organisms cling to the particles. Such tenacity is explained if the organisms are enclosed in the crumb structure and are not lying superficially on the surface, since this would make it far more difficult to dislodge them. The truth of this view is further borne out by the increased number of bacterial colonies that develop on plates from a soil sample which is dissected into the finest possible particles before shaking with the dilution water, instead of merely being sieved in the usual way. It is only reasonable to suppose that such a procedure would liberate more bacteria from the micro-pore spaces, though it is most improbable that it would free the whole population. In a soil which had been dissected the numbers of bacteria that developed were 43 millions per gramme as against 13 millions in the sample treated in the ordinary way.

Recently various workers have developed more direct ways of counting the soil bacteria, which give much higher numbers than are obtained by plating. Conn quotes numbers obtained by his direct method, which may be as much as twenty times higher than those obtained from plate counts on the same soil (2), and other observers give equally striking figures. Taylor, using the ratio method which was devised by Thornton and Gray (45), has obtained results, not yet published, which show a fifty-fold difference between the numbers given by this method and those given by the plate method. On the plot of soil in question the average numbers from five counts made at twenty-four hour intervals were 2836 millions per gramme in the one case as against 53 millions in the other.

The drawback to all the direct methods so far employed is that no distinction can be drawn between cells which are dead and those which are alive ; and the accumulation of dead cells, if they do not disintegrate before the next count is made, may considerably change the number recorded. This may be seen by the comparison of the numbers of bacteria found in pure culture by the plate method and by the direct hæmocytometer method where, again taking the average of five observations, the direct count gave

300 millions per cubic centimetre and the plate count 191. While the plate count is always too low, the direct count is always too high, and the counting method has yet to be devised which will satisfy all criticisms and give an accurate picture of the total number of bacteria which are alive and active in a soil at any given moment.

Probably the main conditioning cause of the numbers of bacteria is the amount of organic matter, since this is the chief source of their energy supply (Table 2).

TABLE 2.—NUMBERS OF BACTERIA IN MILLIONS PER GRAMME, PLATE COUNTS, IN MANURED AND UNMANURED SOILS FROM BROADBALK FIELD.

Date.	Plot 2. F.Y.M. 14 Tons Per Acre.	Plot 3. Unmanured.
July 12, 1922	24·05	15·90
July 13, 1922	23·40	13·80
July 14, 1922	25·35	14·55

In any soil, whether the average numbers are high or low, rapid fluctuations occur not only from day to day but from hour to hour, and this holds good even for soils kept under constant conditions in the laboratory ; on this account isolated observations of the bacterial numbers in a soil may give a very false picture of the general level of activity.

In trying to account for the changes in numbers, or in behaviour, that any members of the soil population undergo, it must always be remembered that not only is the soil itself a complicated environment but that its inhabitants form a very intricate society, in which changes in one group, however they are induced, will in all probability be reflected in other groups. There can be no doubt that in what is commonly regarded as a good soil, which implies a soil ready to give an adequate yield from any ordinary farm crop, there is a delicate balance between the different groups of the population which is perpetually adjusted by the ability of the organisms to adapt themselves to changing conditions.

But an attempt to account for any one definite adjustment on the part of any one group of organisms by referring it to a single influence is likely to be a forlorn hope.

Nevertheless, it is at least interesting to see whether factors such as temperature and moisture, working either independently or together, affect the fluctuations in numbers. Obviously to draw any deductions it is necessary to have a large number of observations and an investigation, which was originally undertaken for another purpose, furnishes suitable material for statistical treatment. The experiments in question involved making daily observations for a year on the numbers of bacteria and protozoa in a field receiving 14 tons of farmyard manure per acre, and the soil temperature and percentage moisture were also recorded. The average number of bacteria in this field soil, as judged by the plate method of counting, over the whole year was 27·7 millions per gramme per day ; if the bacterial numbers are arranged in groups under different temperatures, irrespective of the moisture, and the average for each group is taken, there is no correlation between the average number and the temperature (Table 3). If temperature is disregarded and bac-

TABLE 3.—AVERAGE DAILY NUMBERS OF BACTERIA IN MILLIONS PER GRAMME AND TWELVE-INCH SOIL TEMPERATURES THROUGHOUT THE YEAR. BARNFIELD FARMYARD MANURE PLOT.

Temperature °F.	36-40	41-45	46-50	51-55	56-60	61-70
Bacteria	27·3	30·8	31·6	25·9	24·2	27·5
Number of cases	55	110	38	40	108	13

terial numbers are grouped under different moisture contents, there seems to be a tendency for dry conditions to favour bacterial development (Table 4), though, since the number

TABLE 4.—AVERAGE DAILY NUMBERS OF BACTERIA IN MILLIONS PER GRAMME AND PERCENTAGE MOISTURE IN SOIL THROUGHOUT THE YEAR. BARNFIELD FARMYARD MANURE PLOT.

Percentage moisture	9-11	12-14	15-17	18-20	21-23	24-26
Bacterial numbers	46·3	31·7	33·5	24·7	27·1	21·6
Number of cases	10	19	41	116	171	7

of days on which the soil was relatively dry is outnumbered by those which fall into other groups, it is impossible to be dogmatic on this point.

Although temperature and moisture taken alone do not appear to have much influence on bacterial numbers yet there is the possibility that in combination they may have a direct effect, and that by selecting all the cases where the moisture lies between certain limits, and then averaging the bacterial numbers at high and low temperatures within these limits, significant differences might be brought out.

Such a method can only be applied where the limits are chosen to include a sufficient number of cases to give a representative average; but it is also desirable to have such groups with as narrow a range as possible, and as widely separated from one another. With the material available, which includes daily observations extending over one year on bacterial numbers, moisture content and soil temperature, it is not very easy to fulfil such conditions. The arrangement most satisfactory from this point of view is to contrast a moisture content of 22-23·9 per cent. with one of 18-19·9 per cent., and to consider these together with two temperature ranges of 56°-59·9° and 42°-45·9° Fahrenheit (Table 5).

TABLE 5.—AVERAGE DAILY NUMBERS OF BACTERIA GIVEN IN MILLIONS PER GRAMME AT DIFFERENT TEMPERATURES AND MOISTURES.

PERCENTAGE MOISTURE.

		22·0-23·9.			18·0-19·9.		
		Month.	No. of Cases.	Average Bacteria.	Month.	No. of Cases.	Average Bacteria.
Temperature in °F.	56·0-59·9.	I July August October	10 6 2 }	Actual 18·8 Expectation 19·7	II August September October	4 11 1 }	Actual 15·1 Expectation 18·6
	42·0-45·9.	III January November December	20 4 8 }	Actual 30·5 Expectation 30·1	IV March April October	7 8 1 }	Actual 26·4 Expectation 25·7

There are thus four groups of observations : one when both moisture content and temperature are relatively high (I), another when they are both relatively low (IV), and a third when the temperature is high and the moisture low (II), and a fourth when this condition is reversed (III). When the numbers are grouped like this the higher moistures are undoubtedly accompanied by slightly higher numbers of bacteria at both temperatures, while at both levels of moisture the higher temperatures undoubtedly depress the bacterial numbers. As the highest temperatures recorded are well below those customarily used for the incubation of soil bacteria in the laboratory, which are known to be favourable for growth under these conditions, this is a very anomalous result and one for which there appears to be no explanation.

It is well known that throughout the animal and plant kingdoms life processes show rhythms of various kinds, and that activity is not at a dead level all the year round ; so, in the soil, there are two marked seasons when the numbers of all the groups of micro-organisms are raised to a higher level. Such peaks in the soil population cannot be explained by reference to temperature and moisture, for, in the figures under discussion, one peak occurs in June when the temperature was high and the moisture low, while the other occurs in November when the conditions were reversed (Fig. 1). Is it therefore possible that in Table 5 it so happens that the temperature and moisture groups were by chance largely made up from records obtained during either the peak or the depression periods ? An analysis of the cases from which the averages in this table were obtained shows that this is so, for if the expected average is calculated from the daily averages for the months which are given in Table 6 the results correspond very closely with the actual figures in Table 5. For example, Group I is derived from ten observations in July, when the daily average for the month is 19·3 millions, six in August with a daily average of 16·9

TABLE 6.—AVERAGE DAILY NUMBERS OF BACTERIA IN MILLIONS PER GRAMME OF SOIL FOR EACH MONTH FOR THE YEAR JULY 5, 1920, TO JULY 4, 1921. BARNFIELD FARMYARD MANURE PLOT.

Jan.	Feb.	Mar.	April.	May.	June.	July.	Aug.	Sept.	Oct.	Nov.	Dec.	Total.
26·3	23·9	23·1	29·9	32·1	37·3	19·3	16·9	18·1	30·5	40·9	34·3	27·7

millions, and two in October with a daily average of 30·5 millions. The expected average is therefore 19·7 as against

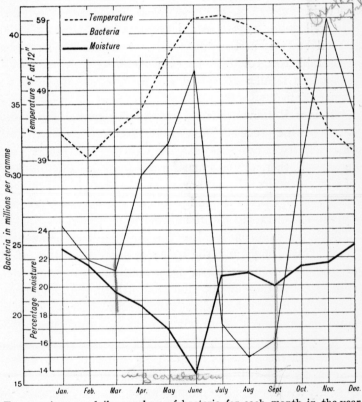

FIG. 1.—Average daily numbers of bacteria for each month in the year July 5, 1920, to July 4, 1921, together with average daily percentage moisture and temperature at 12″ in soil.

the actual 18·8. In Group II the expectation is 18·6 compared with the actual 15·1, while in Groups III and IV the expectation is 30·1 and 25·7 respectively, which are probably not significantly different from the actual figures given for these two groups in Table 5. It is therefore impossible to say whether the seasonal high levels are caused by a combination of temperature and moisture effects, or whether it is inherent in the organisms, and the fact that these temperatures and moistures occur at these seasons is merely a coincidence.

A further attempt to rule out this seasonal effect and thus force a direct issue was made by considering all cases falling around the average temperature and the average moisture for the year, and seeing if, within these groups, any effect could be traced. The average soil temperature for the year in question was 49·4° Fahrenheit, and by taking the range 46°-53° fifty cases were obtained scattered over seven months. When these cases are grouped according to the moisture content into the two ranges 16-19 per cent. and 20-23 per cent. the average numbers of bacteria obtained are 29·3 and 36·2 millions per gramme respectively. It is interesting to compare these figures with the expected average, which again can be obtained by calculation from the daily average for the months given in Table 6.

The expectation in the group with low moisture contents is 29·1 as against the actual 29·3 ; but in the case of the high moisture the expected figure is 29·9 as against the actual 36·2. It seems probable, therefore, that high moisture really is accompanied by some increase in bacterial numbers which is not seen in Table 4 where days at all seasons and at all temperatures are treated together.

The average moisture for the same year was 20·1 per cent., and by taking the range 20-20·9 per cent. fifty-one cases are obtained, which again can be grouped according to higher or lower temperatures. From 39°-49° the actual average number of bacteria was 30·9 millions per gramme, while the expected average is 28·7. From 50°-61° the actual average was 14·7 and the expectation 17·7. Here there is a suggestion that the effect of temperature shown in Tables 3 and 5 is a real one and not merely a reflection of the seasonal rhythms.

There is a further possibility, however, that the numbers of active amœbæ play some part in determining these results, since there is known to be a definite relationship between the numbers of active amœbæ and bacteria evidenced by the fact that on those days when the bacterial numbers rise the numbers of amœbæ usually fall and vice versa. This will be discussed fully in a later chapter, but it is necessary here, before accepting the evidence for the effect of temperature and moisture as valid, to see whether the individual cases which are used in Table 5, were occasions when the numbers of amœbæ were either unduly high or low. Such an examination shows that this explanation does not hold, for when the numbers of active amœbæ are subjected to the same analysis as the bacterial numbers, in no section of the table can differences between the actual and expected bacterial numbers be attributed to the action of exceptional numbers of amœbæ. Probably therefore it may be concluded that a high percentage of moisture encourages bacterial reproduction, while on the whole relatively high temperatures (50°-56° F.) are accompanied by lower numbers.

It may be argued that the problem would be simplified if a complete survey of the bacterial population of a given soil were made, and if the numbers and activities of the different groups were estimated before trying to account for the vagaries of the population as a whole. This is true, but it is at present impracticable.

It is well known that the species of bacteria can be assigned to a few well-defined morphological groups, but, since each group contains species exhibiting very different physiological activities, and since, moreover, in some cases it has been shown that a single species during its life cycle will pass through different morphological stages, a method of classification based on morphology yields little information in a soil survey.

An alternative method, and one which furnishes more valuable information since it gives an idea of the activities of the population, is based on determining the capacity of its various members to carry out the more important chemical changes occurring in soil; for example, the bacteria can be grouped according to their ability to fix atmospheric nitrogen, form ammonia, nitrite or nitrate, denitrify or decompose different forms of carbohydrates. Classifications of this type have been widely used, and many selective media have been devised for making these separations.

The only really efficient method of conducting a soil survey necessitates first of all using a large number of media for preliminary plating of the soil, and picking off all the colonies which appear upon each medium, and deciding later how many of the strains which have been isolated in this way really belong to one and the same species. This method is obviously one which takes a great deal of time, and it is more usual to use a single medium of a type which will allow of the growth of a majority of the organisms. Such a method is not completely satisfactory for, if the medium is too specialised, it cannot be expected that all the bacteria belonging to any one physiological group will grow upon it, or on the other hand, if it is too generalised, many members of other groups will also appear.

In the past a widespread feeling has grown up that bacteria are essentially specialists in respect to their ways of obtaining energy by bringing about specific chemical changes. This is probably largely due to the fact that in its early days the development of bacteriology was based on the study of pathogenic bacteria, where, by the nature of the case, the interest of the investigator was centred upon the effect of the parasite upon a very specialised medium—the tissue of the host—and not upon its possible behaviour in other environments, except in so far as they

2 *

might afford media for laboratory culture apart from the original host. It is noteworthy that when the existence of bacteria was first discovered, Pasteur, Lister, and other early workers recognised that the causation of disease was not the sole function of a pathogenic bacterium, but that it could in many cases live freely in nature apart from its host.

When the vast majority of bacteria which have never adopted a parasitic existence are considered, it is at once evident that they could not carry on the species unless they have considerable powers of adaptation, and the multiplicity of reactions which a well-adapted free living bacterium can initiate helps to make the study of soil economy more intricate.

Among the ammonifying group of bacteria it is possible to find species which, having produced ammonia from peptone, will then oxidise part of it into nitrite; nor is this the end of the story, for under suitable conditions, which are considered in Chapter III, they will then consume the nitrite which they themselves have formed. Such a species is (P 30) which was originally isolated from the filter-bed of a sugar-beet factory and which is almost certainly a soil inhabitant. Sack (40) records a species, *Nitrobacter flavis*, capable of forming nitrite from ammonia and then converting that into nitrate, having first formed the ammonia from peptone.

Nor is such catholicity of behaviour confined to the nitrogen cycle, for there are numerous species which can obtain their energy from a great variety of carbon sources. Thus a species may obtain its energy by decomposing sucrose, lactose, maltose, dextrose, lævulose, galactose, and mannitol, and also from the salts of such organic acids as lactic, acetic, pyruvic, and formic, which may all occur among the decomposition products of the carbohydrates. In fact, those species which grow most readily on all the carbohydrates mentioned are usually those that will grow equally well on the salts of the four organic acids. Of twenty species which readily decomposed the seven carbohydrates 65 per cent. also utilised the four organic acids, while in a general population of 228 species, made up of forms with varying degrees of activities on the carbohydrates, 43 per cent. only were capable of attacking the four organic acids.

A further example of versatility of behaviour is seen in the large number of free-living bacteria which can live as facultative anaerobes compared with the very small number of specialised forms which can only live in a state of complete anaerobicity.

Although the soil is a storehouse for all sorts and conditions of bacteria, yet it is probable that only a few among them are universally distributed, and these will almost certainly be the forms which are able to carry out a diversity of chemical reactions. With them, however, there are in most soils some species of a specialised type, the numbers of which are not great until, for some reason, conditions arise which are favourable to their growth and development. In such a category may be placed the nitrogen-fixing bacterium Azotobacter, which is only found in large numbers after the addition of mannitol, or Nitrosomonas, which demands an alkaline reaction and the absence of organic matter. For reasons such as these it is impossible to predict what the microbiological flora of a soil will be until the type of soil, the manner in which it has been treated, and many other factors have been taken into consideration; but it can be safely asserted that whatever sort of soil is investigated it will be found that the kinds of bacteria and their physiological behaviour will be fitted to the particular peculiarities of that soil.

CHAPTER III.

THE RELATION OF BACTERIA TO NITRITE.

OF all the elements which the plant needs for its healthy existence nitrogen is the only one in which the majority of the supply depends upon the activity of micro-organisms, though this is true of phosphorus to a lesser extent, and whether the supply of available nitrogen in the soil is augmented by fixation from the atmosphere or by the conversion into nitrate of the ammonia which is made by the breakdown of so many organic compounds, these transformations must normally be brought about by micro-organisms. It is customary to speak of the nitrogen cycle in the soil, meaning by this that the nitrogen, which is either fixed from the air or is obtained from the organic residues, becomes ammonia, and in its turn this passes through nitrite to nitrate, and in this soluble form can be absorbed by plant roots, and so comes back to form new plant tissues. Though the account of such a chain of events is true in essentials yet it is misleading, since there are many factors which may interfere with the orderliness of the series. For instance, even before the decomposition of the organic residues has well begun, they may be consumed by worms and insects and either built up at once into animal protoplasm, or excreted back into the soil in the form of simple nitrogenous compounds. The ammonia that ultimately comes from protein is produced by the action of bacteria, both on the protein itself and on the simpler nitrogenous compounds that are formed by its decomposition; but it must be remembered that at every stage the bacteria are abstracting a certain amount of nitrogenous material for the synthesis of their own protoplasm, and a large amount of nitrogen is locked up in this way in the bodies of the micro-organisms which are present in the soil.

In a similar way, when nitrite has been formed from ammonia, it may be used as food by certain bacteria instead of being converted to nitrate ; and again, the whole amount of nitrate that is formed, apart from what leaches out of the soil, will not necessarily go back into plant protoplasm, for it may be reduced by bacterial action and so return to the cycle at an earlier stage. In pure cultures nitrate reduction to nitrite is brought about by many bacteria under perfectly normal conditions of aeration, and presumably in soil the same organisms will be equally active.

Since the first isolation of bacteria from soil it has always been easy to find species which can produce ammonia from nitrogenous organic compounds, but for many years no organisms were found which were capable of converting the ammonia into nitrite or into nitrate, even though Schloesing and Müntz (42) had shown by their experiments that nitrite was formed by biological agencies and not by purely chemical reactions. Nor were they the first observers to make the statement that nitrification was due to the pre-sence of living matter, since in 1873 Müller (31), having ob-served that the ammonia in sewage was very rapidly con-verted to nitric acid, while pure solutions of ammonium salts and also of urea were very stable, suggested that the change in the sewage was probably brought about by a ferment. And even as early as 1862 Pasteur had expressed the opinion that nitrification needed to be studied with this possibility in view.

A survey of the early literature of nitrite formation reveals a number of interesting and frequently contra-dictory views. Schloesing and Müntz, as a result of their work on the purification of sewage, stated that, since chloro-form could put a stop to nitrate formation not only in sewage practice but also in soil, the process must be due to the activity of micro-organisms ; these required organic matter to enable them to form nitrate, and therefore, by implication, organic matter was also needed for nitrite production. Following upon this discovery there was Warington's long-continued work on nitrification (46). He undoubtedly obtained cultures of bacteria from soil which converted ammonium salts into nitrite ; the species in question were also able to make nitrite from organic substances such as asparagine, urine, and milk, but organic matter was not essential, though the addition of sodium bicarbonate or of calcium acetate is recorded as encouraging the reaction. But the bacteria which he succeeded in growing in pure culture on gelatine media never nitrified when they were reintroduced into the appropriate solutions. It is impossible from his papers to decide which species he had, or even whether, during the years that he carried on his work on nitrification, he was always working with the same species, but it is probable that his organisms were similar to the more recently described nitrifiers, and that he did not have cultures of Nitrosomonas.

During the year 1890 papers were published by the Franklands (21) and by Winogradsky (48). The Franklands again record findings very similar to Warington's. Their organisms could grow indefinitely in media which were practically destitute of organic matter, but they would also grow in broth, and when reinoculated from broth into ammoniacal solutions nitrification occurred. Here again it seems likely that they were not working with Nitrosomonas. In the case of such careful workers as Warington and the Franklands it is more probable that they were dealing with a very variable organism, or organisms, than that their results were due to faulty technique.

In his paper published in 1890 Winogradsky first recorded the isolation of the very specialised bacterium, which was afterwards known as *Nitrosomonas europea*.

This organism and its varieties, together with the forms which were described later under the names Nitrosococcus and Nitrospira, have so dominated the minds of soil scientists that for many years the occasional references in the literature to less specialised nitrifiers have either escaped general attention or have tacitly been ascribed to bad technique.

Nitrosomonas was originally isolated by inoculating a drop of nitrifying solution, which had been obtained from soil, into a solution of ammonium sulphate with other salts; this solution had previously been made very alkaline by adding to it 1 per cent of basic ammonium carbonate. On plating out from these cultures bacterial strains were obtained none of which was able to produce nitrite, but after prolonged observation it was found that the nitrifiers were all collected on the solid magnesium carbonate which was present at the bottom of the solution, and that therefore they had not appeared on the plates.

These organisms were found to be incapable of growing in culture media containing organic matter, and since at this period the common culture medium for bacteria was gelatine this probably explains why Nitrosomonas had eluded other workers. Even more surprising than the divergent and frequently contradictory results which have been obtained by reliable workers is the fact that experiments in this field of soil science carried out in the same laboratory by the same workers and under apparently standardised conditions often gave equally puzzling results. At Rothamsted repeated attempts to obtain Nitrosomonas have met with no success, though the evidence that it exists in many other soils is undoubted; and further, in every recorded case, its behaviour is typical in that, when it is grown in the laboratory under the conditions laid down by Winogradsky, strong nitrification ensues.

This is far from being the case with the unspecialised species of bacteria which have been isolated at Rothamsted, and, if earlier workers were dealing with similar strains,

many of the discrepancies in the results can be explained.
The first among these species were obtained from soil (14),
but a still larger number were isolated during an investigation
which necessitated the separation and subsequent identi-
fication of a large number of strains from biological filters.
Among these strains there were a large number of species
which were constant in behaviour except as regards their
powers of nitrification. These, however, showed considerable
variability, since, though by some species nitrite was invariably produced when ammonia was present, with other
species the same solution would produce nitrite on one
occasion and not on another, with no apparent reason for
the difference in behaviour.

None of these species can be compared with Nitrosomonas as regards their individual power to produce nitrite ;
the greatest amount that has ever been obtained from
ammonium salts in a pure culture being 3·2 parts of nitrogen per million and on most occasions the amount was
lower. There are, however, enough species which can produce these small amounts to make the cumulative effect
a large one.

Because of their variability it is difficult to dogmatise
about their behaviour but, nevertheless, a certain amount
of definite information concerning them has been acquired.
Although there is no exact relation between their numbers
in a culture and the amount of nitrite produced yet there is
a general relation, for, as might be expected, the increase of
numbers during the period of growth from the inoculation to
the first maximum is accompanied by an increase in nitrite
in almost all cases (Table 7).

Considering the later period when the bacterial numbers
are no longer steadily increasing, but have begun to fluctuate, it would be expected that if the relationship were rigid,
an increase in numbers would be reflected in the amount of
nitrite found, while a decrease would leave the nitrite unaffected. This, however, does not occur, for not only does

TABLE 7.—CORRELATION OF BACTERIAL NUMBERS WITH NITRITE PRODUC-
TION FOR FOUR SPECIES OF BACTERIA. A + SIGN DENOTES AN
INCREASE AND A — SIGN A DECREASE. THE NUMBERS OF BACTERIA
ARE GIVEN FIRST.

	+ +	+ −	− +	− −
Growth period	68	15	0	0
Later period .	38	57	60	75

the nitrite vary in quantity, both increasing and decreasing,
but the changes in amount bear no relationship to the changes
in bacterial numbers.

Further, although nitrite is frequently reduced in amount
or entirely removed from the culture, no nitrate is produced,
and only one species has hitherto been found which gives
rise to ammonia as the result of the removal of nitrite.
Among these species there has never been any evidence of
the production of gaseous nitrogen though in some other
forms this is known to occur. The only conclusion that can
be drawn from these results is that the organisms are using
the nitrite that they themselves have produced as material
for building up their own protoplasm. If, instead of starting
the culture with ammonium salts and leaving the organisms
to make their own nitrite, sodium nitrite is given instead
of ammonia as the source of the nitrogen supply, the
organisms still use it. It is true that because nitrite
is commonly regarded as a poison only dilute solutions of
not more than 0·0016 per cent. have been given, yet the
results have been so uniform and have occurred on so many
occasions that there can be no doubt that these are due to
bacterial action and not to other influences. It is difficult
to ascribe the peculiarities of behaviour that occur in the
later periods of cultural growth to an intrinsic cause, and it
is far more likely that they are due to some chemical factor
in the environment. In the experiments where sodium
nitrite was used, and the nitrite disappearance was marked,
the carbon-nitrogen ratio was always high, and therefore it

appears likely that the carbon-nitrogen ratio is the conditioning agent.

That this is the case has been shown by subsequent work,
and to illustrate this point an experiment may be quoted.
Two species which are known to consume nitrite were
inoculated into a mineral salt solution containing 0·0008
per cent. of sodium nitrite, and sucrose was added so that
the carbon-nitrogen ratio was only 2·5 : 1·0. During three
days the nitrite remained untouched, so that at the end of
this period the ratio was raised to 89 : 1 by the addition of
appropriate quantities of nitrite and sugar, with the result
that, on the following day, no nitrite was present. The ratio
was again in a similar manner raised and again the nitrite
disappeared. Exactly the same result was obtained at a
ratio of 19 : 1 ; but when the ratio was raised to 12 : 1 the
nitrite was only very slightly reduced in quantity. The
further addition of sucrose, however, caused the complete
disappearance of the nitrite within twenty-four hours.

Another experiment in which the ratios ranged from
5 to 40 bore out these results, for at a ratio of 20 the nitrite
had nearly disappeared, while at 30 and 40 no trace was left ;
below 20 the amount of nitrite was unchanged. The numbers
of bacteria in these three cultures were identical (Table 8).

TABLE 8.—AMOUNTS OF NITRITE IN MEDIA WITH DIFFERENT CARBON-
NITROGEN RATIOS AFTER TWENTY-FOUR HOURS' BACTERIAL GROWTH.
INITIAL NITRITE 1·6 GRAMME PER MILLION.

$\frac{C}{N}$ Ratio.	Nitrite Expressed in Grammes of Nitrogen per Million.	Bacterial Numbers, Millions per Cubic Centimetre.
5	1·6	48
10	1·6	34
15	1·6	46
20	0·1	42
30	0·025	50
40	0	40

There is evidence that though the carbon-nitrogen ratio
is always important in determining the disappearance of

nitrite it does not of necessity operate at the same level for all species.

The results so far quoted are obtained with a species which is capable of utilising nitrite at a lower ratio than any other, namely, 19 : 1, nevertheless even this figure is higher than is found in normal soil where usually the carbon-nitrogen ratio is round about 10. Therefore, if an analogy is drawn from laboratory cultures to soil, which is admittedly unsafe, nitrite will not be removed from a normal soil by bacterial agency.

Turning from the disappearance of nitrite to its formation this is found to occur on a number of ammonium salts, both of the inorganic and organic acids. There are species which make nitrite on all the salts presented to them, while others are not so catholic in their tastes. Thus among those known to produce the larger quantities of nitrite one, Z 20, forms it on sulphate, carbonate, phosphate, acetate, lactate, formate, and pyruvate, while another, P 30, gives no nitrite from acetate and formate, and a third, P 15, gives none on sulphate, carbonate, acetate, and formate though on the other salts the reaction is strong. In all these cases the carbon-nitrogen ratio was 8 or less, sucrose having been added to the inorganic salts to provide the necessary carbon. It is possible that the addition of sucrose in some cases defeated its own ends, for with those species that form acid by the splitting of the carbohydrate the pH value may fall to 4·5 or lower, and the presence of this degree of acidity may cause the disappearance of nitrite by purely chemical means. For example, if, in a culture where acid conditions have been induced by bacterial growth, the solution is sterilised and sodium nitrite is added at the rate of 0·7 milligrammes to the litre, it is found that within the first few hours no change in the nitrite occurs, but that after forty-eight hours it disappears. This result is not consistent, since there are numerous records of nitrite being found in cultures where the pH value is lower than 5·0 ; it is of course possible that a time factor is

involved, and that a high degree of acidity will always decompose the nitrite after a sufficient lapse of time, but in any
case it is a fact which may help to explain in some cases
the vagaries of the nitrite organisms. A species may form
appreciable amounts of nitrite from the ammonium salts of
lactic, acetic, formic, and pyruvic acids, and also from
ammonium sulphate in the presence of lactose, which is only
very slightly decomposed and where the pH value in conse-
quence does not fall below 6·5, but when more readily
decomposable carbohydrates are present with the ammonium sulphate, and an acidity of 4·5 is produced, no
nitrite can be detected, though it is quite possible that it
has been formed but has not been able to persist.

All the evidence points to the fact that a low carbon-
nitrogen ratio encourages nitrite formation, but a definite
pronouncement on this point is difficult when such small
amounts are in question. That nitrite is formed is undoubted,
but small increases, though they are probably genuine where
the technique is sufficiently careful, can only be accepted
tentatively, since the Greiss-Ilosva test is very sensitive
and even traces of nitrite are recorded. Therefore any
medium in which the organisms would produce nitrite in
larger amounts would be preferable to the synthetic media
so far employed. For example, using a mixture of sucrose
and ammonium sulphate in mineral salts and adjusting the
carbon-nitrogen ratio to 3, 9, 15, 21, 27 and 54, while keeping
the amount of ammonia constant, no nitrite could be found in
the last four cultures while it was produced in the first where
the ratio of carbon to nitrogen was 3 ; and though the
quantity did not rise above 0·2 grammes of nitrite nitrogen
per million, yet it remained constant at this amount. In
the culture where the carbon-nitrogen ratio was 9 a similar
amount was formed, which subsequently disappeared. In
all the cultures the pH value was not materially lowered.
The bacterial numbers never reached a high level in these
cultures, which probably explains the small amount of nitrite

produced, and, if numbers are the criterion of healthy growth, the use of a more nutritive medium is suggested.

In the search for the ideal medium for nitrification various organic substances have been tried. On using a 1 per cent. solution of peptone in which the control gave negative results to the tests for ammonia, nitrite, and nitrate, after three days' growth 0·4 grammes of nitrite nitrogen per million was found. Parallel cultures with ammonium sulphate and dextrose gave much smaller quantities. As the exact chemical composition of peptone is unknown it would be preferable to use simpler substances provided they would give equally good results. With tryosin and alanine, however, the nitrite produced was still less than in the case of peptone, though it was definitely more than when the organisms were growing in cultures containing inorganic nitrogen sources only.

Urea, which has a carbon-nitrogen ratio of 1 : 2, proved to be an unsatisfactory medium for nitrite formation ; but urine yields larger amounts of nitrite than does peptone, though if the amount of carbon is increased by adding small amounts of sucrose the quantity of nitrite which is formed is distinctly less (Table 9). Since urine is so much better as a medium

TABLE 9.—AMOUNTS OF NITRITE FORMED IN URINE AFTER FOUR DAYS' BACTERIAL GROWTH BY TWO SPECIES IN PURE CULTURE WITH DIFFERENT CARBON-NITROGEN RATIOS. (RATIOS CALCULATED ON THE ASSUMPTION THAT A NORMAL URINE IS 1 : 2.)

C : N Ratio.	Nitrite expressed in Grammes of Nitrogen per Million.	
	P 15.	Fr 21.
$\frac{1}{2}$	0·3	3·2
1	0·05	0·2
2	0·025	0·15

for this purpose than is urea, it suggests the possibility that there may be substances present in the natural product which promote nitrite formation, and these would be lacking

in the synthetic medium containing urea, although this
is made up in the ordinary mineral salt solution containing
four salts. This suggestion is borne out by the fact that if
very small amounts of blood clot are added to the synthetic
medium the nitrite formation is increased, while similar
additions to the urine are without any effect (Table 10).

TABLE 10.—AMOUNTS OF NITRITE FORMED BY SPECIES FR 21 IN PURE
  CULTURE IN URINE AND UREA SOLUTION, WITH AND WITHOUT THE
  ADDITION OF BLOOD CLOT, AFTER SEVEN DAYS' GROWTH.

No. of Parallel Culture.	Amounts of Nitrite in Grammes of Nitrogen per Million.			
	Urine Alone.	Urine + Blood.	Urea Alone.	Urea + Blood.
1	1·55	1·55	0	0·15
2	1·55	1·55	0	0·15
3	0·75	1·55	0	0·35

Three species of bacteria have been used for the most part
on the media containing organic compounds as the source
of nitrogen for nitrite formation ; of these, the species Z 20
is probably the most active nitrifier, and, as has already been
stated, it is the one which can carry out this process on the
greatest number of compounds. On urine it can produce
6·4 grammes of nitrogen per million in five days. Of the
other two species, P 15 is a good nitrifier, but it also is one
of the forms which very readily under suitable conditions
demolishes the nitrite it has made. The third species,
Fr 21, has an interesting history, and is possibly a more
specialised form than are the others. It was isolated from
a sample of peat given to us by H. S. Fremlin, who has worked
upon nitrification for many years (22, 23) ; this peat had been
used for a considerable period of time in a urinal, and had
been found to give a high degree of purification since the
filtered liquid remained odourless, and contained large
amounts of both nitrites and nitrates. From this material
Fremlin himself had isolated an organism which he has
described under the name of the nitroso-bacterium (24) ;

this species when it is growing well can nitrify 10 cubic centimetres of a one in fifty solution of ammonium sulphate completely in two and a half months, and the same amount of undiluted ammoniacal urine in less than a fortnight. The species Fr 21 is, however, different from Fremlin's nitroso-bacterium, and is not quite such an efficient nitrifier; nevertheless it, too, even in pure culture, can purify urine to a very considerable degree during its filtration through peat into which the bacterium has been inoculated.

It seems probable that with intensive culture on suitable media, Fr 21 would develop into as good a nitrifier as the nitroso-bacterium, which has been subjected to a long series of rigorously selective culturing. At the present time, however, the nitroso-bacterium shares with Nitrosomonas the first place as an effective nitrifier, and has, moreover, a very much wider sphere of action.

Judging by the results which have so far been obtained it is a very small minority of bacteria in nature, that, given suitable conditions, are not able to interfere with the nitrite part of the so-called nitrogen cycle; either they can make small quantities of nitrite from ammonium salts, or they can remove nitrite, or in many cases they can perform both reactions according to the conditions prevailing at the time. Of forty-four species which have been exhaustively studied as regards their ability to make or remove nitrite in pure culture only one has been found that gives no reaction in either direction.

CHAPTER IV.

ALTHOUGH the carbon in the soil is never destined to serve directly as plant food it is nevertheless a vital factor in plant nutrition, for it is the carbon that supplies the necessary energy for the bacteria to carry out the various chemical transformations by which the supply of nitrate in the soil is maintained. It is the amount of organic matter which determines whether a soil can support few or many bacteria, and so the amount of carbon dioxide given off from any soil might be expected to bear some relation to its microbiological activity. Unfortunately, repeated experiments by many observers have shown that once soil is taken from the field and placed under artificial conditions, no matter how carefully they may be adjusted to replicate natural ones, it is no longer strictly comparable with the same soil in the field. In spite of this, however, valuable information can be obtained by laboratory experiments, where it is possible to estimate the amount of carbon dioxide evolved from a known weight of soil and to try to relate it to the micro-flora and fauna which is present. The soils of the classical fields at Rothamsted afford good material for such a study, since they are divided into plots, each of which has received the same manurial treatment and has grown the same crop for many years, and here, if anywhere, clear-cut results might be expected.

Probably the most satisfactory laboratory method of obtaining a measure of the carbon dioxide production of a soil is to draw air, which has been freed fron carbon dioxide, over a known weight of soil kept at a constant temperature in a water bath, and to estimate the carbon dioxide evolved by the well-known Pettenkoffer method; by this means observations can be made at regular intervals without disturbing the soil in any way. Daily records on parallel samples show that the evolution of carbon dioxide is by no means a straightforward process, and that it is controlled from within the soil and not by external causes, since these are kept constant. It is possible, on occasion, to find that duplicate samples give strikingly similar results, while

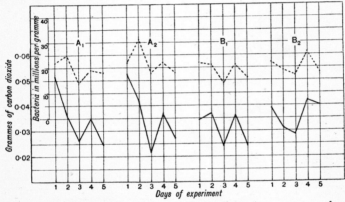

FIG. 2.—Amounts of carbon dioxide given off by 200 grammes of soil from Broadbalk, plot 2, and bacterial numbers. The figures are corrected for dry soil.
A_1 and A_2 are parallel experiments on one sample, B_1 and B_2 are parallels on a sample taken 8 yards away from A.

at other times there are equally striking discrepancies. Fig. 2 shows the results of daily estimations of carbon dioxide and of bacterial numbers on samples from a field soil receiving 14 tons a year of farmyard manure; the samples A and B were taken 8 yards apart and each was put up in duplicate. Not only do all four specimens of soil behave in the same general way, although there are differences between the two samples, but the amounts of carbon dioxide closely follow the changes in bacterial numbers. On the other hand, the parallel estimations shown in Fig. 3,

3 *

which were obtained from a sample taken from the same
plot a fortnight later, neither show similarity of behaviour nor
correspondence between the bacterial numbers and the output of carbon dioxide, though the general level of carbon
dioxide production in the two parallels of this experiment
is the same. The amount of carbon dioxide recorded from
this same soil on the two different dates was entirely different,
being lower on the second, although the bacteria were higher.

If all the daily observations on the amount of carbon

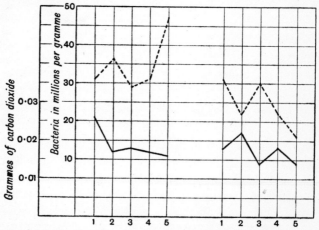

Fig. 3.—Amounts of carbon dioxide given off on five successive days by
200 grammes of soil from Broadbalk, plot 2, and bacterial numbers.
The figures are corrected for dry soil. Parallel experiments from the
same soil sample. The dotted line represents bacterial numbers.

dioxide given off from the farmyard manured plot on
Broadbalk are arranged in groups (Table 11), and the bacteria
corresponding to these amounts are averaged, there is no
indication of any correlation between them, since the average
numbers of bacteria are approximately the same entirely
irrespective of the quantity of carbon dioxide. The daily
amounts of carbon dioxide evolved from equal quantities
of the same soil may differ so much that probably a fairer
picture of the capability of the soil in this direction is obtained by averaging the output for several days, and here,

TABLE 11.—AMOUNTS OF CARBON DIOXIDE PRODUCED DAILY FROM A PLOT RECEIVING 14 TONS OF DUNG PER ACRE PER YEAR COMPARED WITH THE NUMBER OF BACTERIA.

Grammes of Carbon Dioxide from 200 Grammes Soil in twenty-four Hours.	Average Number of Bacteria in Millions per Gramme of Soil.	Number of Cases.
0-005	15·4	16
0·005-0·010	17·8	24
0·010-0·015	18·1	23
0·015-0·020	13·5	14
0·020-0·025	17·3	11
0·025-0·030	16·9	7
0·030-0·035	18·8	4
0·035-0·040	—	0
0·040-0·045	17·0	2

as an arbitary figure, five days has been adopted. Accepting this convention, and comparing the amounts of carbon dioxide given off by the soil from four of the plots on Broadbalk, it will be seen (Table 12) that the one receiving farmyard manure gives the same result as plot 16 which receives a dressing of minerals with 86 lb. of nitrogen as nitrate of soda per acre, and is not very much better than plot 7 which is treated with minerals and 86 lb. of nitrogen as sulphate of ammonia, or than plot 3 which has received no manure since 1839 ; the bacteria, however, are definitely more numerous on plot 2 than they are on the others. The different occasions on which estimations have been made on the soil from plot 2 show a very wide range of amounts of carbon dioxide ; for a sample taken in April gave a daily average of as little as 0·006, while samples taken in January gave six times as much. The moisture content of these samples was 22·8 in January, while in May it was exceedingly low, being only 6·4 per cent. ; the average bacterial numbers in the two sets of samples were 20 million in both cases. At first sight this lack of correspondence is surprising ; but when it is borne in mind that not only is the bacterial population very heterogeneous, but that so also are the carbon compounds which are present, such a lack of correspondence is only to be expected. A mythical soil containing only one source of carbon, and that a simple one, and also harbouring only

TABLE 12.—GRAMMES OF CARBON DIOXIDE GIVEN OFF BY 200 GRAMMES OF DRY BROADBALK SOILS IN TWENTY-FOUR HOURS AVERAGED FOR FIVE DAYS, WITH THE AVERAGE NUMBER OF BACTERIA IN MILLIONS PER GRAMME OF DRY SOIL.

Month.	Plot 2. Farmyard Manure.		Plot 3. Unmanured.		Plot 7. Sulphate of Ammonia.		Plot 16. Nitrate of Soda.	
	Carbon Dioxide.	Bacteria.	Carbon Dioxide.	Bacteria.	Carbon Dioxide	Bacteria.	Carbon Dioxide.	Bacteria.
May .	0·005	21	0·004	11	—	—	—	—
	0·007	22	0·004	10	—	—	—	—
February	0·016	16	—	—	0·013	13	—	—
	0·017	16	—	—	0·012	15	—	—
March .	0·020	23	—	—	—	—	0·022	11
	0·024	20	—	—	—	—	0·021	12

one species of bacterium would inevitably give a high correlation between carbon dioxide production and bacterial numbers ; but where the carbon is present under numerous guises, and where any single compound may be treated differently by any of the innumerable species of bacteria, a clear-cut relationship will only occur occasionally, and probably only when there is a preponderance of one particular species of organism.

A material which approximates to such a mythical soil

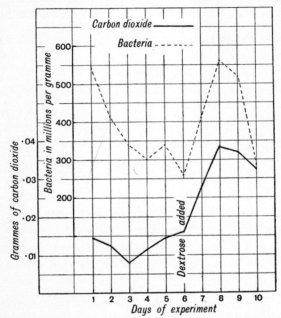

FIG. 4.—Carbon dioxide given off from 100 cubic centimetres of soil extract and numbers of bacteria before and after the addition of dextrose.

is found in sand to which the appropriate nutrient ingredients have been added together with a selected species of bacterium. The results of an experiment with these materials are shown in Fig. 4, where the nutrient medium used was soil extract, and though the correspondence between the bacterial number and the carbon dioxide output is fairly close, yet even under these simplified conditions it is not complete. When, however, on the sixth day dextrose to the amount of 0·2 per cent. was given, the bacterial numbers and the carbon dioxide evolution both rose considerably, and showed a striking parallelism.   Out of 107 daily observations made on sand cultures there were only thirty-one occasions when the bacterial numbers and carbon dioxide production did not move in the same direction, and, after working out the probabilities of this being due to chance as deduced by the χ^2 test (20) the correlation between them is found to be significant.

A large number of results have been obtained from inoculated sand and also from inoculated Rothamsted soils which had previously been sterilised, yet, although in a general way there is agreement between the bacterial numbers and the carbon dioxide produced, there is no exact numerical relationship between the two, in the sense that twice the number of bacteria, even of the same species, will necessarily produce twice the amount of carbon dioxide.   The explanation of this seems to be that there is a difference in the efficiency of the individual bacterial cell which is governed by such factors as the density of the population and the condition of the organism, that is as to whether it is actively growing and reproducing or whether it has passed through the growing phase.   On the whole the bacteria are more efficient as producers of carbon dioxide when their numbers are not rising and less so when they are actually reproducing. It has been suggested that during the reproductive period the energy of the bacteria is primarily devoted to building up new protoplasm, and that it is when the period of rapid growth is over that the organism liberates more carbon dioxide (10).   Further, the efficiency of an individual bacterium varies with the density of the population, being greater when the population is small (Table 13).   Similar results were obtained by Telegdy-Kovats using similar materials (44).

The inverse relationship between numbers of bacteria and their individual efficiency is not confined to carbon dioxide production only, since it is also true for ammonia

TABLE 13.—AMOUNT OF CARBON DIOXIDE IN GRAMMES GIVEN OFF BY 1000 MILLION BACTERIA.

Numbers of Bacteria in Millions Per Gramme.

	No. of Cases.	0-200	No. of Cases.	200-400.	No. of Cases.	400-600.	No. of Cases.	600-800.	No. of Cases.	Over 800.
Soils—										
Farmyard manured	2	·000245	2	·000140	7	·000126	3	·000098	33	·000039
Unmanured . .	12	·000149	9	·000053	1	·000055	2	·000049	2	·000049
NaNO$_3$ . .	24	·000365	10	·000058	5	·000062	1	·000029	—	—
(NH$_4$)$_2$SO$_4$.	16	·000190	7	·000091	—	—	—	—	1	·000041
Sands—										
Peptone .	4	·000092	11	·000080	9	·000042	5	·000105	5	·000063
Soil extract .	28	·000259	8	·000068	5	·000058	—	—	7	·000017
NaNO$_3$ . .	14	·000558	1	·000112	—	—	—	—	—	—
(NH$_4$)$_2$SO$_4$.	19	·000790	—	—	—	—	—	—	—	—

production in pure cultures (28, 29), and it seems probable that it is of universal occurrence. That the density of the population should affect efficiency, even where there is no question of overcrowding, seems inexplicable ; but there is abundant evidence that in a circumscribed community of any kind there are obscure laws which govern individual behaviour, whether the community consists of bacteria or protozoa, or of more highly organised animals.

For a long time bacteria have been classified to some extent by their behaviour on various carbohydrates, that is to say by their ability to produce acid, or acid and gas, from these compounds. But this behaviour is of more than academic interest, for the relation of the bacteria in soil to the carbon compounds occurring there has already been shown to be of fundamental importance, and the organism which can obtain energy from the largest number of different types of compounds is the one which stands the best chance as a soil dweller. Among the bacterial species which were obtained from biological filters (p. 26) the great majority must have originally come from soil, for the effluent which was being treated on the filters came from a beet-sugar factory, and the water had previously been used for floating the roots into the factory and for washing off the soil with which they are often heavily coated. As the effluent also contained about 2 per cent. of sucrose it is to be expected that the population would be automatically selected, with the result that the species capable of oxidising carbohydrates and their derivatives predominate. An investigation of a population of this nature affords an opportunity of discovering whether the various steps in carbohydrate decomposition are carried out by specialised groups of bacteria or whether the different species composing the population are each capable, when the occasion arises, of performing the various chemical transformations. For example sucrose, when it is hydrolysed, yields dextrose and lævulose, which in their turn can ultimately be converted into carbon dioxide and water, and whether all the stages in these reactions can be performed by a single species of bacterium, or whether successive specialised forms are needed to complete the process is a matter of considerable practical interest. There is the further question as to which is the commoner of these two types of decomposition.

Taking as a criterion of specialisation the ability to split only one of the six sugars which were used in this experiment, highly specialised forms are comparatively rare, since out of 259 species there were only ten that could attack sucrose and no other sugar, eight for lactose, ten for dextrose, five for galactose, eleven for lævulose, and six for maltose. The two possible extremes of behaviour occur on the one hand with the forms that utilise all six sugars, and on the other those that will touch none of them (Table 14). Of the former there are twenty-

TABLE 14.

	Total Number.	Number of Sugars Split by Bacterial Species.						
		6	5	4	3	2	1	0
Species from sugar filters .	259	23	29	30	42	43	50	42
Species from milk tanks .	44	8	10	8	5	8	2	3

three, while of the latter forty-two, many of these, however, do make use of the salts of such acids as acetic, formic, pyruvic, and lactic. The general range of activities of a number of free living bacteria is shown in Table 15. There is a definite distinction between the mono-saccharoses and the disaccharoses, and of the former lævulose is the most readily available for bacterial food. Undoubtedly in a filter receiving effluent of the type in question there would be a good deal of lævulose and dextrose derived from the sucrose, and so it might be argued that there would be an unusual

TABLE 15.—NUMBER OF SPECIES SPLITTING EACH COMPOUND IRRESPECTIVE OF THEIR ACTION ON THE OTHER COMPOUNDS.

	Sucrose.	Lactose.	Dextrose.	Galactose.	Lævulose.	Maltose.	Mannitol.	Lactate.	Acetate.	Formate.	Pyruvate.
Species from sugar filters	101	83	121	119	136	90	93	157	212	203	210
Species from milk tanks .	18	17	35	25	33	28	35	—	—	—	—

predominance of bacteria that are able to split these sugars. But the species isolated from an entirely different source showed a very similar distribution on the sugars, except for the fact that maltose was more often attacked (Table 15). In this case the bacteria came from a tank which was being used for investigations on the purification of effluent containing milk, and which therefore contained a mixture of fat, casein and lactose, and their derivatives. Among these species there was a greater degree of activity among the sugars as a whole (Table 14), evidenced by the fact that 59 per cent. occur in the first three columns of the table, that is, they are capable of decomposing four, five or six of the sugars, while in the sugar strains only 31 per cent. occur in these columns, but lævulose and dextrose were still the most frequently attacked of the sugars (Table 15).

Among the bacteria isolated from these sources there are some species which can utilise the disaccharoses and yet be without action on their monosaccharose derivatives. It might be supposed that when a bacterium is capable of breaking up one sugar it would also inevitably be able to carry out a similar process on certain others ; for example, one would expect that ability to split maltose would be correlated with the capacity to split dextrose, and the same would be expected to hold for the derivatives of sucrose and lactose. Maltose, however, is more often correlated with lævulose or with galactose among the species obtained

TABLE 16.—ABILITY OF SAME SPECIES OF BACTERIUM TO SPLIT BOTH MEMBERS OF A PAIR OF SUGARS. THE LESS FREQUENTLY DECOMPOSED SUGAR (FROM TABLE 15) IS GIVEN FIRST IN EACH PAIR.

		Sucrose Maltose	Lactose Maltose	Dextrose Maltose	Galactose Maltose	Lævulose Maltose	Sucrose Lactose	Dextrose Lactose	Galactose Lactose	Lævulose Lactose	Dextrose Sucrose	Galactose Sucrose	Lævulose Sucrose	Dextrose Galactose	Lævulose Dextrose	Lævulose Galactose
Species from sugar filters	Number of times the less frequently decomposed member of pair is split	90	83	90	90	90	83	83	83	83	101	101	101	119	121	119
	Number of times both sugars are split by same organism	46	46	57	62	72	41	44	50	59	69	61	72	87	90	88
	Percentage	51	55	63	69	80	49	53	60	71	68	60	71	73	74	74
Species from milk tanks	Number of times the less frequently decomposed member of pair is split	18	17	28	25	28	17	17	17	17	18	18	18	25	33	25
	Number of times both sugars are split by same organism	16*	16	28	20*	27	9	16	15	16	17	12	18	24	32*	21
	Percentage	89	94	100	80	96	53	94	88	94	94	67	100	96	97	84

* In these cases the less frequently decomposed sugar is the second member of the pair.

in the sugar filters than it is with dextrose from the point of view of bacterial activity, and the same may be said for lactose (Table 16), but with sucrose, the numbers of organisms that split lævulose and dextrose, as well as this sugar, are definitely higher than obtains for the other three sugars. Apart from this, in the sugar strains, there is very little evidence of correlation between any two sugars, which may lend support to the conclusion that bacterial behaviour and chemical structure bear little relationship to each other.

With the strains derived from the milk tanks the situation is different, and there is evidence of considerable correlation between all the different pairs of sugars, with the exception of lactose with sucrose, and sucrose with galactose, and possibly of galactose with maltose and lævulose. If more strains were available it is probable that the degree of correlation would be decreased.

In testing the behaviour of the same bacterial species on the organic acids, the ammonium salt of the four following acids was used : lactic, acetic, formic, and pyruvic. It has already been said that the bacteria which split none of the sugars are able to act on these salts ; thus there were fourteen which can grow on all four of them, twelve on three, fifteen on two, and one on only one (Table 17) ; but

TABLE 17.—BEHAVIOUR OF SPECIES SPLITTING ALL SIX SUGARS AND NO SUGARS WITH THE ORGANIC SALTS.

Species Splitting.	Number of Species Splitting 4, 3, 2, 1, 0 Organic Acids.				
	4	3	2	1	0
6 sugars .	13	6	3	1	0
0 sugars .	14	12	15	1	0

when the species capable of utilising all the six sugars are classified in the same way, those that act upon all four acids are still in a considerable majority.

This ability to attack a variety of compounds has already been mentioned in Chapter II, but it is of such significance in practical bacteriology that it is worth stressing, for it means that there are species of bacteria which can probably carry out the complete decomposition of comparatively intricate organic compounds in pure culture. The course of events in a culture containing one of the species, which is a very active sugar splitter, in a medium in which sucrose was the only source of carbon, shows the type of behaviour which may be expected. In an experiment in which the medium contained 0·08094 grammes of carbon as sucrose at the beginning, 0·0256 grammes of carbon were given off as carbon dioxide in eight days, and during this period the pH changed from 7·2 to 4·6 and then back to 7·7 ; after a further five days carbon dioxide containing 0·0128 grammes of carbon was given off, and a new type of decomposition had set in for the cultures were frothing vigorously. Here there is evidence of at least three types of behaviour on the part of the same organism ; the first when the sugar is split with the formation of acid, the second when the acid disappears, and the third when the substances formed from the decomposition of the acids are, in their turn, acted upon with the evolution of gas.

The figures which are given in Table 15 show that the salts of the organic acids are on the whole very much more

TABLE 18.—NUMBER OF TIMES THAT THE SAME SPECIES OF BACTERIUM SPLITS EACH ORGANIC ACID AND EACH SUGAR, EXPRESSED AS PERCENTAGES OF THE TOTAL NUMBER OF TIMES THAT THE LESS FREQUENTLY DECOMPOSED MEMBER OF THE PAIR IS SPLIT. THE AMMONIUM SALT OF THE ACID WAS USED IN EACH CASE.

	Lactate.	Acetate.	Formate.	Pyruvate.
Sucrose .	64	81	82	74
Lactose .	66	78	80	86
Maltose .	70	78	88	79
Dextrose .	70	87	88	82
Lævulose .	60	84	86	87
Galactose .	69	86	79	81

readily utilised by these soil bacteria than are the sugars, and ability to split the acids is accompanied by a corresponding ability to split the sugars except in the case of lactate where this is not so marked (Table 18) ; there is also evidence (Table 19) that if a bacterium can act upon

TABLE 19.—NUMBER OF TIMES THAT THE SAME SPECIES OF BACTERIUM SPLITS BOTH MEMBERS OF A PAIR OF ORGANIC ACIDS, EXPRESSED AS PERCENTAGES OF THE TOTAL NUMBER OF TIMES THAT THE LESS FREQUENTLY DECOMPOSED MEMBER OF THE PAIR IS SPLIT. THE AMMONIUM SALT OF THE ACID WAS USED IN EACH CASE.

Lactate Acetate	Lactate Formate.	Lactate Pyruvate.	Acetate Formate.	Acetate Pyruvate.	Formate Pyruvate.
86	85	85	81	85	80

one organic acid it will probably be able to act upon one or more of the others, though in no case is there a complete correlation between any two substances.

CHAPTER V.

THE GROWTH OF PROTOZOA IN PURE CULTURE.

In a pure culture of micro-organisms grown under laboratory conditions the curve of growth always follows the same general course ; that is there is an initial period of slow growth and reproduction followed by one during which the volume of protoplasm increases more rapidly ; then, as the maximum number of organisms that the particular culture can support is approached, there is a tailing off in the reproductive rate and this is succeeded by irregular alternations of death and reproduction (Fig. 5). There are of course numerous factors which can limit the size of the maximum population which any culture can maintain ; but in spite of all limitations the actual sigmoid shape of the growth curve persists. By the nature of the case any reaction which begins and ends more slowly than it is carried on during the intermediate period will give a sigmoid curve, when the rate is plotted against time. For example, the speed of a train starting at one station and stopping at a further one would, if plotted, fall upon a sigmoid curve. To the biologist the interest in the sigmoid shape of the growth curve lies in the question as to whether there is something during the initial " lag " period corresponding to the gradually increasing pressure of steam in the engine, and whether, during the final stages of growth, there is something that corresponds with the shutting off of steam and the application of brakes, as the engine reaches its journey's end. Alternatively it may be argued that the sigmoid growth curve does not give a true picture of the life

4

of the culture, but has been obtained from too scanty observations during the critical periods. According to Robertson (36) the reproductive rate of each individual cell in a culture is enhanced by the neighbourhood of others, so that the reproductive rate increases according to the number of individual cells per unit volume of nutrient material. This effect of contiguous cells on the rate of reproduction he called allelocatalysis. Pushed to the logical

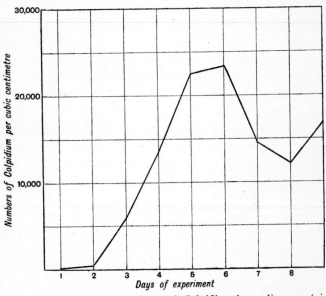

Fig. 5.—Growth of a mass culture of *Colpidium* in medium containing mineral salts and ammonium glycero-phosphate.

conclusion this means, as Robertson stated, that if a single cell is isolated into too large a volume of nutrient fluid it will die without reproduction having taken place, the critical volume being about 1 cubic centimetre. The evidence for allelocatalysis has been disputed, for with Colpidium a relatively large number of organisms divide no more quickly than does a single organism in a drop of the same size, and moreover one organism will readily grow and populate a volume as large as 10 cubic centimetres (7). Peskett

(34, 35), in his work on yeast, has also obtained no evidence for the existence of this phenomenon.

If allelocatalysis were true then the lag period would be satisfactorily explained by it, but the evidence is too inconclusive and the explanation must be sought elsewhere. When a sub-culture is made the age of the parent culture in hours is known, but the physiological age of the individual organisms that it contains is a matter of pure conjecture. The usual way of stating the age of a mass culture is to refer to the number of hours or days which have elapsed since it was first made. This is a useful convention, but it is not biologically sound, since time is not the sole factor concerned in the ageing of either a culture or, indeed, of an organism.

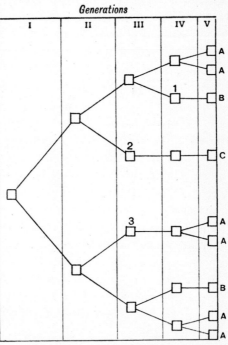

FIG. 6.—Diagram showing possible irregularities of reproduction in the descendants of a single cell through five generations.

If the view is accepted that the life of an individual organism starts at its formation from the parent cell and ends when it, in its turn, divides to form new daughter cells then, after a relatively short period, even a culture coming from a single cell will contain individuals of very different ages. The accompanying diagram (Fig. 6) may make this point clear. In the fifth generation there are only nine cells instead of the sixteen which should have been present, and of these the cells marked A are the youngest, while those marked B are a generation older, and C is the oldest of all. Why the cells numbered 1, 2, and 3 should not divide when their twin cells do so is a matter for conjecture ; but the fact remains that this type of thing is characteristic of all cultures. When the problem is regarded from a different point of view, and the age of a cell is judged by its reproductive potentiality, then it is probable that the different ages of the cells in a mass culture are in part responsible for the initial lag period in its growth.

If sub-cultures are made from a mass culture at regular intervals there is a gradual increase in the lag period with the age of the parent culture, until finally the numbers drop significantly below those originally inoculated (Fig. 7). The fact that when old parent cultures are used there is an initial death-rate among the inoculated cells renders it extremely likely that the slight lag that is seen even in the thirty-six hour culture is due to a lowering of the initial numbers by death, though the actual drop is masked in this case by the vigorous reproduction that is going on among the other cells. The logical deduction is that, if a transference of cells could be made so that no death followed inoculation into a foreign medium, the lag period would disappear entirely, and the line of growth during the first part of its course would be straight.

This lag following inoculation may also be accounted for, not only by the death of some of the cells owing to the shock of being transferred to fresh medium, but also by the presence of some cells which, owing to their physiological senescence, will inevitably die without reproduction.

In any culture of protozoa there are always a certain number of cells which are physiologically senescent, for even in a young culture, if counts are made at sufficiently short intervals of time, the curve does not rise steadily, but from time to time shows decreases which can only be accounted

for by death (Fig. 8). That there is a heavier death-rate
when an old parent culture is used is probably due to an
interaction of both these factors ; that is, to the relatively

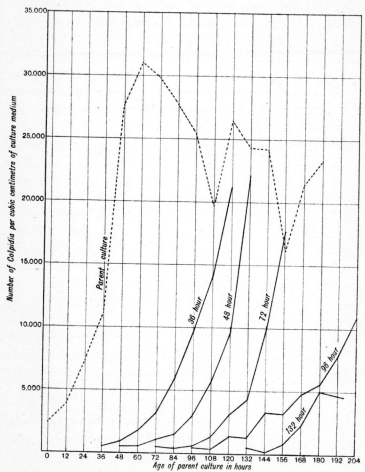

FIG. 7.—Growth of sub-cultures of *Colpidium colpoda* made at intervals
   from an ageing parent culture. The numbers of cells in each sub-
   culture are only shown up to the first maximum.

high percentage of senescent cells and also to the fact that
there is a very much greater difference between the medium
of the old parent culture and the medium of the sub-culture

owing to the amount of growth that has taken place in the former, and the shock on transference is therefore greater and causes the immediate death of the unhealthy cells which might otherwise have lingered on in the culture.

The effect of a staling medium undoubtedly has a marked action on the rate of reproduction, for constant renewal of the medium leads to a higher reproductive rate than occurs in a control culture. Two experiments with the flagellate

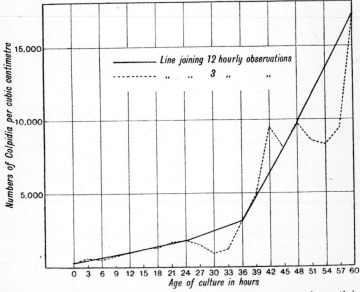

FIG. 8.—Three-hourly observations during the first 60 hours of growth in a culture of *Colpidium* made from a 24-hour-old parent culture.

Oicomonas termo may be quoted in illustration of this point. In the one, three parallel cultures were centrifuged daily and the supernatant fluid was replaced by fresh medium of the original consistency, while the medium of the control culture was left unchanged (Table 20). During the first nine days the inhibiting effect of the gradual staling is seen when the experimental cultures are compared with the control. The second experiment further substantiates this point, for here medium which had supported a large popula-

TABLE 20.—REPRODUCTIVE RATE IN THREE PARALLEL CULTURES OF *Oicomonas termo* IN WHICH THE MEDIUM WAS CHANGED DAILY COMPARED WITH THE RATE IN A CONTROL CULTURE.

Days of Experiment.	Control.	Treated Cultures.		
1	3·91	2·13	2·58	3·32
2	2·54	3·73	3·91	4·70
3	2·51	2·64	2·93	1·19
4	0	0	0	0
5	0·08	0·36	0	0·30
6	0	0	0	0
7	0	1·65	1·29	0·47
8	0	1·37	0·70	0·28
9	0	1·17	1·24	1·12
Total reproductive rate.	9·04	13·05	12·65	11·38

tion of Oicomonas for three days was added, after boiling, in quantities ranging from 2·5 per cent. to 4·5 per cent., to six fresh sub-cultures of the same organism. In this case an average reproductive rate of 5·31 was obtained in the control after two days' growth, while the six treated cultures in the same time gave an average reproductive rate of 2·29. These experiments undoubtedly show that there is something inimical to reproduction in an old culture medium, that has supported growth, even when the quantity is as small as it was in the experiment just described ; but it is not safe to assume that the organism itself, in the above case *Oicomonas termo*, is the cause of this effect, since it is known that both bacteria and their products can have a profound influence on protozoan growth.

The amœba *Nægleria gruberi* grows satisfactorily with *B. mycoides*, since it can use this bacterium as a source of food ; but, when such bacterial cells were thoroughly ground with hay infusion in a glass bacterial mill, and 50 per cent. of the resulting liquid, after filtration, was added to fresh hay infusion into which *N. gruberi* had been inoculated, the behaviour of the amœba in this culture presented a very different picture from that shown in a parallel culture in hay infusion alone.

In the control (Fig. 9) the end of the initial growth period was reached on the third day, and of the total population of 307,500 amœbæ, 57,500 were encysted. The toxin culture, however, was in comparison much less active, and

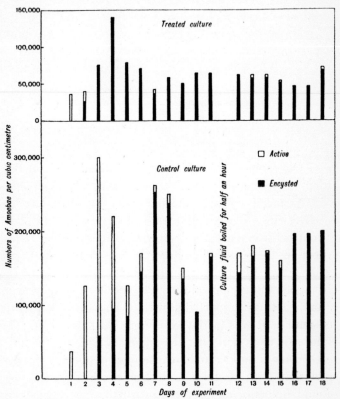

FIG. 9.—Numbers of active and encysted amœbæ in hay infusion (control), and in hay infusion + 50 per cent. hay infusion containing the filtrable products of crushed cells of *B. mycoides* (treated). On the eleventh day both cultures were centrifuged, the supernatant fluid was boiled, and the amœbæ were returned to the boiled liquids.

the initial peak was not only delayed by twenty-four hours but was definitely lower, the total number present being 140,000, of which all were encysted. After these periods the numbers in both cultures agreed in falling, and in the toxin culture remained more or less constant to the end of the experiment, while, with one exception, 100 per cent. of the individuals were in the form of cysts ; in the control, although the percentage of cysts still remained high, there is definite evidence that reproduction was still taking place since the numbers alternately rose and fell.

As it was evident, from this experiment, that the toxin was exercising an inhibiting influence this culture was centrifuged to collect the amœbæ and the supernatant fluid was boiled for half an hour ; to this material the amœbæ were

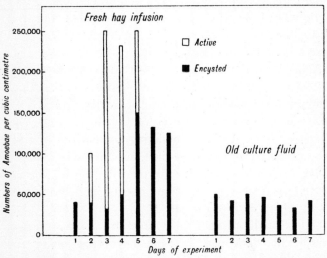

FIG. 10.—Numbers of amœbæ after inoculating the centrifuged cells from the treated culture in Fig. 9 into fresh hay infusion and old boiled culture fluid.

returned and the experiment was continued (Fig. 9). Boiling had no appreciable effect.

The control culture was similarly treated and behaved in the same manner. After seven days the cultures were again centrifuged and boiled, and on this occasion the amœbæ from each culture were divided, and while half were returned to their own fluid the other half were put into sterilised hay infusion (Fig. 10). Again, in the case of the original toxin solution, boiling had no effect.

The original control, which had also been boiled, gave much the same result, though there was an initial excystment, accompanied by slight reproduction, after which it behaved like the toxin culture, but on the whole there was a greater degree of activity.

The cysts from both cultures which had been put into new medium showed an entirely different picture as regards activity, for not only did considerable excystation occur, but this was accompanied by a reproductive rate of 0·94 in one case (control) and 2·59 in the other (toxin).

Judging from the results obtained from the treated culture the effect of *B. mycoides* toxin was undoubtedly to depress the whole level of activity.

Apart from the internal causes that make the organisms in a culture fall out of step in their divisions, there are external ones which affect all the cells equally, and which may make the same number of divisions occupy a much shorter or longer period, thereby rendering comparison of cultures of the same age, as judged by time, unsound unless an exactly similar environment has been provided. Both food supply and temperature are important agents in determining the rate at which divisions occur.

Quite small changes in temperature are sufficient to bring about changes in the rate of reproduction in various species of protozoa. Maltaux and Massart (27) showed this to be the case in *Chilomonas paramœcium*, where in four-day old cultures an increase in temperature from 14° C. to 35° C. resulted in a decrease in the time of division of the organism from thirty-three to five minutes (Table 21). In *Colpidium colpoda* (6), where the individual cells are very much larger and the division rate is relatively slow, the reproductive rate at 19° C. was 5·1 in four days, while in the same experiment parallel cultures at 25° C. showed a reproductive rate of 6·0 in the same time. Woodruff and Baitsell (50) concluded that, judging by the results they obtained with *Paramœcium aurelia*, the rate of cell

TABLE 21.—TIMES OF DIVISION IN *Chilomonas paramœcium* AT DIFFERENT TEMPERATURES (AFTER MALTAUX AND MASSART).

Temperature in °C.	Time of Division in Minutes.
14	33·00
17	25·00
19	22·35
20	17·15
22	15·00
24	13·35
26	12·00
28	8·30
30	6·15
35	5·00

division is influenced by temperature just in the same way as are chemical reactions. In any case it is necessary in all comparative work to keep the temperature constant within very narrow limits. As with all other animals so also with the protozoa the amount of the food supply largely determines the amount of growth, and, in some cases, the effect of feeding a starved culture in which the individual cells are very small with a suspension of suitable bacteria is positively startling. Fig. 11 shows outline camera lucida drawings of *Colpidium colpoda*, all at the same magnification, made from animals which had been supplied with different amounts of the same bacterium to provide food. Group A are starved forms, while B are those from the same culture twenty-four hours after they had been supplied with food, and the individuals in Group C are from the same pure line, though not from the same culture, where the nutrient had been pushed up to a maximum. In all probability the drawings in A and C represent the extreme limits of size for this species.

In Fig. 11 a typical *Colpidium colpoda* from the same strain is shown at D ; this cell was taken from a culture in which the active phase of reproduction was over, but in which there was still an ample food supply, and the specimens which are found in natural habitats usually approximate to this type. Incidentally, the fact that it is possible to get such extremes in a pure line of the same species shows how little reliance can be placed on either size or shape as a diagnostic character for either varieties or species.

Apart from the increase in the size of the individual cells as the food supply increases there is also a definite relationship between the amount of food and the reproductive rate. In the case of Colpidium there is a steady rise in the rate of division which goes hand in hand with the increase in the ratio of the numbers of bacteria to the

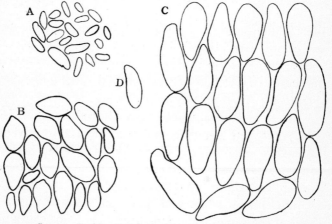

FIG. 11.—Camera lucida drawings (× 524) of individuals of *Colpidium colpoda* taken at random from cultures with different amounts of bacteria.

individual Colpidium (Table 22). The increase in numbers is not directly proportional to the increasing ratio, and with the data available it is not possible to say whether the actual increase in protoplasm would be directly proportional to the ratio or not ; but it is possible that if the actual volume of protoplasm were known, and not only the reproductive rate, that the curve connecting bacterial ratio and the mass of Colpidia which is obtained when the figures in Table 22 are plotted, would be resolved into a straight line.

In the case of the flagellate *Heteromita globosa* there

TABLE 22.—REPRODUCTIVE RATE IN TWENTY-FOUR HOURS OF *Colpidium colpoda* IN PURE CULTURE WITH " YB " BACTERIA AT DIFFERENT BACTERIAL RATIOS.

Ratio.	Number of Cases.	Reproductive Rate.
0-1000	8	0·04
1000-2000	8	0·08
2000-4000	9	0·11
4000-8000	26	0·24
8000-16000	18	0·45
16000-32000	21	0·71
32000-64000	15	1·47
64000-128000	14	2·45
128000-256000	16	2·88
256000-512000	5	3·94
512000-1024000	6	4·10
1024000-2048000	3	5·30

is no appreciable difference in the rate of reproduction at the different ratios shown in Table 23. Since, however,

TABLE 23.—REPRODUCTIVE RATE IN TWENTY-FOUR HOURS OF MASS CULTURES OF *Heteromita globosa* AT DIFFERENT BACTERIAL RATIOS.

Ratio.	Number of Cases.	Reproductive Rate.
0-200000	38	7·1
200000-400000	51	7·2
400000-600000	27	6·8
600000-800000	27	6·8
800000-1000000	21	6·9

this organism is much smaller than Colpidium, the constant reproductive rate is probably due to the fact that throughout the experiments the amount of food was always in excess of the requirements of the animals, and therefore no increase of reproduction with increased food supply could be expected.

Exactly the same relationship that is found in Colpidium between bacterial ratio and reproductive rate is also found in the amœba *Hartmanella hyalina* (Table 24). In this particular case the observations were made on single cells isolated from mass cultures, and therefore there are no low ratios included in the results, since, when only one cell is

TABLE 24.—REPRODUCTIVE RATE IN TWENTY-FOUR HOURS OF SINGLE CELLS OF *Hartmanella hyalina* IN PURE CULTURE WITH TWO SPECIES OF BACTERIA AND AT DIFFERENT BACTERIAL RATIOS.

Ratio.	Bacterial Species.			
	"YB."		"SE."	
	Number of Cases.	R.R.	Number of Cases.	R.R.
0-400000	34	3·4	34	1·0
400000-800000	40	4·2	55	1·5
800000-1200000	40	4·5	47	1·9
1200000-1600000	10	4·7	23	2·4
1600000-2000000	9	5·0	11	2·7

isolated, even a low number of bacteria gives a relatively high figure for the ratio. In *Nægleria gruberi* the reproductive rate is very much lower at the same bacterial ratio, being 1·9 at a ratio of 0 to 400,000 and 2·8 at the highest ratio of 1,600,000 to 2,000,000. The food supply in this case being " YB." There is evidence to show that this difference in reproductive rate is not due to " YB " being a less suitable food for Nægleria than it is for Hartmanella, but to a real physiological difference between the two amœbæ as regards their rate of division.

With an amœba such as Hartmanella it is possible to measure its mass with a reasonable degree of accuracy, for owing to its comparatively slow movement camera lucida drawings can be made, and if such drawings are made when the animal is extended its thickness is relatively constant. When the mass is calculated in every case from the average of ten such drawings the error is small.

Neither the increase in size in a well-fed culture nor the decrease in a starved one proceeds steadily (Fig. 12) ; there are vicissitudes and the animal may become unexpectedly larger or smaller. These unexpected changes can be accounted for by the fact that, in order to get a constant supply of food, the amœba would have had to move continually at a steady rate through a medium in which the bacteria were evenly distributed ; any one who has watched the behaviour of these small soil amœbæ knows that such conditions never are fulfilled, because in the first place the animal's movements are erratic, and in the

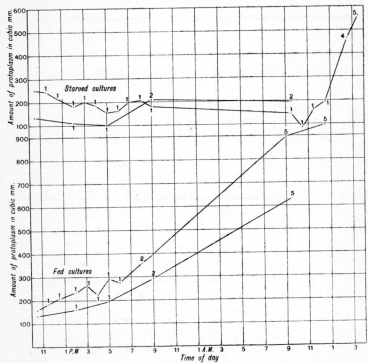

Fig. 12.—Changes in the amount of protoplasm in cultures starting from single amœbæ (*Hartmanells hyalina*). The numbers at each point on the curves refer to the number of individuals which were present at the time of observation.

second, the mere presence of the moving cell prevents a really homogeneous distribution of the bacteria. Nevertheless, omitting the points in the figure where there is apparently a decrease in the mass, the line representing the growth of the fed amœba is very nearly a straight one. In the case of the starved cultures the mass decreased more or less steadily for twenty-four hours, but at the end of this period, when one of the animals was fed, its increase in mass again approximated to a straight line.

Apart from the differences caused in the growth of a protozoan population by the amount of food provided, the quality of the food also exerts an influence, and different species of bacteria appear to have different nutritive values (Table 24). The bacterial species " YB " and " SE " are indistinguishable under the microscope, since they are of the same size and shape, yet their nutritive value, as judged by the rate of reproduction of the amœba feeding on them, is by no means the same. This is a true feeding effect, for if it were due to the production by the bacteria of waste products having a bad effect on the growth of the amœba, then the introduction of such products into a culture without the actual bacteria would have the same effect. But this does not happen, for in an experiment in which 50 per cent. of the medium in which the amœbæ were grown consisted of a filtrate made from a twenty-four-hour-old culture of " SE " bacteria, the average reproductive rate in the control was 4·95 and in the treated cultures at the same bacterial ratio the rate was 4·97. Both cultures were fed with " YB " bacteria, and the filtrate of " SE " bacteria obviously had no effect upon the reproduction of the amœbæ.

It is frequently assumed that in any pure line of protozoa division always takes place at approximately the same size, but this is not the case where the food supply is not the same in quantity or quality. In *Colpidium colpoda* dividing individuals were found in all the cultures represented in Fig. 11 ; while the sizes at which Hartmanella divides also vary within wide limits. For example, individuals well fed with " YB " bacteria, on the average divide at about 270 μ^3, while those which are sparsely fed with the same species divide at about 190 μ^3. When " SE " is the source of food well-fed animals divide at about 190 μ^3, that is at approximately the same size as occurs in cultures poorly fed with

" YB." All the evidence shows that in the case of the protozoa whose natural food is bacteria the numbers in a culture
are controlled by the numbers of bacteria available ; and,
as has been already suggested for soil, the number of bacteria
depends ultimately upon the supply of carbon. Therefore
in any one medium it is not surprising to find that, irrespective of the numbers of protozoa inoculated, the maximum which is ultimately reached is about the same (Fig. 13).

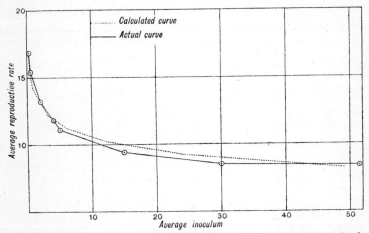

FIG. 13.—Average reproductive rates in pure cultures of *Colpidium colpoda*
from the inoculum to the first maximum, using inocula varying from
0·2 to 51·5 cells per cubic centimetre.
The dotted line is the curve obtained by calculating the reproductive rate
from the average inoculum to the average first maximum (10·2 for
12·3 cells per c.c.) and assuming that every time the inoculum is halved
the rate is increased by 1·0.

Taking 15,000 Colpidia per cubic centimetre to be the
average maximum population which can be supported under
the conditions of the experiment, the number of bacteria
required for each animal to divide once, when this maximum number had been reached, would be in the neighbourhood of 600,000,000 per cubic centimetre, and this is
a number which is very rarely attained in this medium.
The composition of the medium thus automatically controls
the final density of the protozoan population.

In the great majority of protozoa the formation of cysts is a regular occurrence, and whatever the history of a culture may have been during its development, cysts will begin to be formed at some period during its growth, until ultimately, if the culture is kept long enough, nothing but cysts will remain, death having overtaken those individuals which for any reason were unable to encyst.

It must be remembered that cysts among the protozoa, though all of them happen to be protective, are formed in different ways ; there are those in which a protective envelope forms around a single organism which eventually emerges apparently unchanged, those in which during the encystment period a single organism divides into four or more daughter cells, and thirdly, the type found in such forms as Oicomonas, where two individuals fuse and are enclosed in a conjugation cyst from which only one individual emerges.   Though often called reproductive this is not a true reproductive cyst, yet it is possible that as a result of such conjugation the power of reproduction in the new individual is increased. There are, of course, variants of all these three types of encystment.

A considerable diversity of opinion exists as to what are the causes of cyst formation.   In many text-books the teleological statement is made that cysts are formed to tide the animal over a time when conditions are so bad that the active forms could not survive ; but although cysts undoubtedly do serve this purpose the statement does not cover all the facts.   Various agencies have been suggested as the causes of cyst formation, and it is possible that different species are differently affected ; drying up of the medium has been stated to encourage encystation in some forms, and the presence of metabolic products in others ; these two may obviously be really one and the same thing, since evaporation will increase the concentration of any products which may be present in solution.   Temperature, lack of food, and hydrogen ion concentration have also been regarded as primary causes of encystation in some species, as well as combinations of two or more of any of these factors.

It must, however, be borne in mind that there is considerable evidence to show that encystation is a normal and regular occurrence in the life-cycle of many of the protozoa ; and a consideration of the encysted life of the common soil forms, under normal field conditions, strongly supports this view. It is impossible to imagine that the average percentages of cysts which are shown in Table 25, built up as

TABLE 25.—AVERAGE DAILY PERCENTAGE OF CYSTS OF FOUR SPECIES OF PROTOZOA PRESENT IN THE SOIL FOR EACH MONTH OF THE YEAR, JULY 5TH, 1920, TO JULY 4TH, 1921.

	Nægleria.	Heteromita.	Cercomonas.	Oicomonas.
January . . .	37	40	23	48
February . . .	43	36	31	46
March . . .	38	41	32	49
April . . .	34	34	35	47
May . . .	33	38	31	45
June	56	42	30	55
July	67	44	31	50
August . . .	68	43	31	37
September . . .	47	51	29	49
October . . .	59	49	26	53
November . . .	35	43	22	44
December . . .	56	44	32	50

they are from records of daily observations in which the percentage of cysts may fluctuate from 0 to 100 per cent. of the total numbers, can be explained on any assumption but that encystment is a normal stage in the animal's life history. This being the case it is unlikely that external conditions alone are responsible for causing encystation, though they may very probably help to determine the time at which the cysts are produced. Further light is thrown on this point by encystment in pure cultures.

The chain of events in a culture in which cyst formation occurs is well illustrated in Fig. 14, where the course of growth is shown from the isolation of a single active amœba to the point at which the culture contains almost 100 per cent. cysts. The numbers of amœbæ show a steady increase up to the fifth day, while cyst formation begins on the fourth day and steadily increases up to the end of the experiment. From the fifth to the sixth day the number of active amœbæ decreased by 68, while the number of cysts increased by 44, and it is a problem, of which at present there is no solution, to explain what was the difference between the 44 that encysted and the 24 that died.

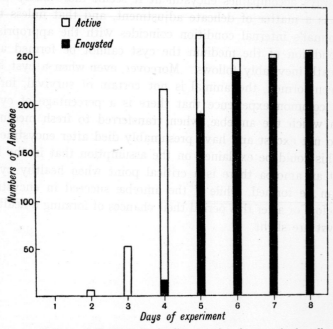

FIG. 14.—Culture of *Hartmanella hyalina* starting from a single cell and ending with almost 100 per cent. of the individuals encysted.

In the more complicated case of a mass culture there is the same sequence of events (Fig. 9, control culture) ; it is interesting to compare this culture from the point of view of cyst formation with the parallel one already described, to which a filtered suspension of crushed cells of *B. mycoides* had been added (Fig. 9, treated culture). Judging from the results obtained from this second culture the effect of the added filtrate, in addition to depressing the whole level of activity, was to encourage cyst formation. A consideration of Figs. 9, 10, 14 suggests that, during an amœba's career, it may at any moment be faced with a set of conditions which make reproduction temporarily impossible and compel it to encyst or die. Encystment cannot be an easy process for, if it were, the whole of the culture would form cysts without any appreciable drop in numbers. But since death nearly always accompanies encystment it seems more likely that it is a matter of delicate adjustment, and that unless the animal's internal condition coincides with the appropriate condition of the medium the cyst cannot be formed and death inevitably follows. Moreover, even when a cyst has been formed, the animal is not certain of survival, for it is common experience that there is a percentage of cysts in which the amœbæ, when transferred to fresh medium, do not excyst and have presumably died after encystment. This could be explained on the assumption that in the life of an amœba there is a critical point when healthy cysts can be formed, while if the amœbæ succeed in encysting before or after this period their chances of forming a healthy cyst are slight.

CHAPTER VI.

THE BEHAVIOUR OF PROTOZOA IN SOIL.

THE Protozoa are divided into four classes : the Rhizopoda, which includes all the amœbæ, the Flagellata, the Ciliata, and the Sporozoa, these last are of no interest in the present connection as they are exclusively parasitic, and, even if their spores find a temporary resting-place in the soil after liberation from one host and before they gain access to another, they can play no part in the soil economy. The other three classes, however, all have their active soil representatives. The members of the class Rhizopoda, which is regarded as being the most primitive group among the Protozoa, are usually defined as unicellular organisms in which there are no permanent organs of locomotion at any stage, that is to say, the cell moves by extruding ever-changing masses of protoplasm, or pseudopodia, from the body. In this class the members may further be classified according to the presence or absence of a shell, and, where the shell is present, the pseudopodia are thrust out of one or more openings ; both these types occur in soils. In the class Flagellata, on the other hand, there are permanent organs of locomotion in the adult condition, which take the form of long threads of protoplasm, or flagella, and these propel the animal through any liquid medium. There is evidence that these two classes, the Rhizopoda and the Flagellata, are derived from some common ancestral stock, and species exist which can only be arbitrarily assigned to one or the other class, since they possess features which ally them with both. The third class, the Ciliata, contains forms which are more highly specialised, and which are on the whole larger than those belonging to the other two free-living groups. For purposes of classification their essential feature is the possession of minute vibrating hairs, or cilia, by which they swim.

Regarded critically from the point of view of their suitability to life in the soil the small Rhizopoda are obviously well adapted to the physical conditions ; so are the majority of the Flagellata, since they too are for the most part of small size, but many of the Ciliata must be barred from colonising any normal soil because they are too large to move freely in the restricted moisture that is available. Further, it is unlikely that any large species which does not form cysts, such as Paramœcium, ever succeeds in having any but the most temporary existence in a field soil.

Any soil, if it is suitably examined, will almost certainly yield species of several types of Protozoa, even though at first sight it may appear to be a most unpromising medium for their growth. Some idea of the extent of their occurrence can be obtained from the map facing this page, where the localities are marked from which soils were sent to Rothamsted for examination in the course of a study of protozoan distribution (41). In no case was any soil devoid of protozoa, although the range of both soil and climatic conditions in the various places was very great ; for the samples in this investigation were drawn from a variety of soil types, which included laterites, sands, clays, peats, and loams of all sorts, and the pH values ranged from 3·7 to 9·3, while the total amounts of nitrogen lay between 0·005 and 2·85 per cent. The latitudes of the places of origin varied from the equator, through sub-tropical and temperate regions, to the Arctic and Antarctic zones, and the limits of rainfall were very wide ; Granada, with its 200 inches per annum, providing the upper limit. Soils bearing all types of vegetation were included, and even those which were recorded as barren still possessed a protozoan population.

A similar wide distribution is found in the many samples which have been examined by different observers from the various soil types and formations in Russia, Hungary, Roumania, France, and other European countries. In most soils the protozoa occur in greatest numbers at a depth of about 10 to 12 centimetres ; and below this they are very scarce, though in special cases where the sub-soil is very deep they may be found at lower depths in considerable numbers. Thus in a deep Kenya soil even at 4 feet below the surface protozoa were present.

It is probable that in the soils which are subjected to extremes of climatic conditions the protozoa spend most of their lives as cysts, and only lead an active life for relatively brief periods during which in most cases they succeed in attaining fairly high numbers.

The number of different species which occurs in any one soil sample varies very much ; Sandon (41) mentions forty-six as being the greatest number of forms found and one as the least. He further states that 250 species in all have been recorded from soil, but that many of these occur sporadically ; the great majority are found in other situations as well, especially in stagnant water, infusions of various kinds, sewage, and, in fact, in all places where there is decomposing organic matter. Twenty-one of the 250 species, however, have been recorded from soil only, and, among these, there are even three new genera, representatives of which have hitherto never been found in any other locality. It seems likely that in time all the forms now regarded as being confined to soil will be discovered in other habitats. Those which are ubiquitous in soil include species of three genera of flagellates, *Heteromita globosa*, *Oikomonas termo*, *Cercomonas spp.*, two species of ciliates, *Colpoda cucullus* and *Colpoda steinii*, and two amœbæ, *Nægleria gruberi* and *Hartmanella hyalina*, but even among these there are anomalies in the distribution. For instance, the two amœbæ, Nægleria and Hartmanella, very rarely occur in the same soil at the same time, though one or the other is almost invariably a dominant species in any normal field soil ; in the same field, at one time, Nægleria, and at another Hartmanella, may be the genus which is found, and in neighbouring fields at the same time Nægleria may occur in one and Hartmanella in the other. These results are the more curious since in cultures the two forms flourish under identical conditions, they are, moreover, almost indistinguishable in the active amœboid state though the cysts are obviously different. One of the differences between the two species is their rate of reproduction (p. 62).

There are also protozoa which flourish in many of the other situations in which the ubiquitous soil forms are found and yet which are by no means common in soil. Such a form is *Bodo saltans*, which in infusions is of very common occurrence and therefore, since it can on occasion live in soil, might be expected to have a wide distribution ; but Sandon (41) records it in only four of his soils, and although it has been reported by other workers it never appears to be common. Numerous cases of this kind might be cited, showing how much still remains to be discovered about the needs and behaviour of these animals.

Among the protozoa there is a very wide range of substances that can be used as food, and there are different methods of feeding. Thus there are the saprozoic species which can obtain their nourishment, not from organised material, but from the solution produced from the decomposed remains of animals and plants ; it is rare for this type of feeding to be used exclusively by any one species among the soil forms, though it seems likely that on occasion some of the flagellates can resort to it. On the other hand, there are the holozoic species which ingest solid food, and there are numerous substances which can be used, such as detritus, dead and living bacteria, yeasts, fungal spores, algæ and lastly protozoa of a suitable size, either in the encysted or active state.

The type of food that is used by any individual species is naturally governed to some extent by size ; and, among the smaller forms, bacteria and small yeasts probably make up the bulk of the food, while the consumption of other protozoa and of large algæ and yeasts is practically confined to the ciliates and larger amœbæ. All species of bacteria are not equally suitable as food supplies, and this also applies to fungi, algæ and yeasts ; some are apparently wholly inedible, while others are not accepted unless they are the only food available, nor do different protozoan species of necessity use the same strains of bacteria. With these animals, as with more highly organised forms, it is true to say that one man's meat is another man's poison.

Thus Oehler (33), using five different small amœbæ, found considerable differences in their food reactions. None of them would live on fungal spores, green algæ or diatoms, nor would they accept such substances as egg yolk or blood corpuscles ; two of them grew on *Saccharomyces exiguus* and on another yeast, but the other three would not. Four of the amœbæ were approximately of the same size, while the fifth was very much smaller, and of the four larger ones three ate small amœbæ, which were refused by the fourth.

The differences in the reactions to killed food materials were also marked, since two of these species readily digested dead bacteria, which had been killed by autoclaving for one hour at 130° C., while the other species scarcely grew at all under these conditions. One of them, however, could grow well with *B. coli* which had been killed by heating at 56° C. for one-and-a-half hours. The smallest amœba, though it could not grow with any of these dead bacteria, did do so with *B. fluorescens* when it was killed by heating at 45° C. for one-and-a-half hours. The fifth species did not grow under any of these conditions, and would not accept any dead bacteria.

Among other workers in this field Severtzova (43), working with a single species of soil amœba, tested its reaction with twenty-six species of bacteria, twelve moulds, four yeasts, and two actinomycetes, all of them being soil forms. Of these, nine species of bacteria, nine moulds, two yeasts and both of the actinomycetes were unsuitable. The seventeen bacterial species with which the amœba grew included species showing very varied chemical reactions. In one or two cases Severtzova describes true selective feeding as distinct from mere inability to grow with a certain food material; for example, the amœba would only ingest Azotobacter when other bacteria were not present, and *Cladosporium herbarum*, though eaten readily when it was the only available food, was not accepted if more attractive organisms were provided.

In counting the protozoa in soil a dilution method is used, and since the cultures that are made from each dilution are examined microscopically it is possible, not only to make a total count, but also to make one of each species separately. In addition to this by making a second count, on a sample that has previously been treated with dilute acid to kill the active protozoa, leaving the cysts unharmed, the numbers of both active and cystic organisms can be separately determined (3, 16).

The protozoa in the soil are exposed to exactly the same external conditions as are the bacteria, and daily counts made over a long period show the same kind of fluctuation in numbers.

The average daily numbers for the months in the year 1920-1921 show very marked differences (Fig. 15). As in the case of bacteria there are two periods of high numbers, which also coincide with high activity, while, during the months of July and August and to a less extent September, there is a period of extreme depression.

The numbers of the protozoa have been treated in the same way as were the bacterial numbers to see whether temperature or moisture, taken separately or together, are in any way responsible for the changes in numbers.

Temperature (Table 26) or moisture (Table 27), when considered separately, are apparently without effect, except in the case of Nægleria, where the higher temperatures seem to lower both the total number and the activity.

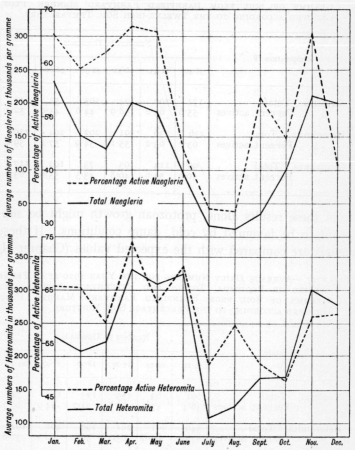

FIG. 15.—Total numbers and percentage of active forms of *Heteromita globosa* and *Nægleria gruberi* in Barnfield dunged plot. Daily average for each month in the year July 5, 1920, to July 4, 1921.

When the numbers are treated in the same manner as was described for the bacteria on page 14, it again appears that the higher temperatures are definitely depressing

(Table 28), and this is particularly the case when they are combined with the higher moisture content ; in fact, judging

TABLE 26.—AVERAGE DAILY NUMBERS FOR THE YEAR 1920-21 OF THREE SPECIES OF PROTOZOA, TOTALS AND PERCENTAGE ACTIVES, PER GRAMME OF SOIL FROM BARNFIELD FARMYARD MANURE PLOT, GROUPED ACCORDING TO THE TWELVE-INCH SOIL TEMPERATURE.

Temperature °F.	Numbers in Thousands.					
	36-40.	41-45.	46-50.	51-55	56-60.	61-65.
Nægleria. Total . .	172	200	174	103	52	41
,, Per cent. actives	55·6	63·2	58·9	44·6	45·9	32·3
Heteromita. Total . .	236	236	301	202	204	239
,, Per cent. actives	63·7	63·2	55·1	54·9	57·2	59·4
Oicomonas. Total . .	99	114	95	73	102	117
,, Per cent. actives	50·3	54·6	46·8	43·5	55·6	63·7

from these results alone, protozoan growth might be supposed to be favoured by cold, damp conditions. If these figures are compared with the expected values (Chapter II,

TABLE 27.—AVERAGE DAILY NUMBERS FOR THE YEAR 1920-21 OF THREE SPECIES OF PROTOZOA, TOTALS AND PERCENTAGE ACTIVES, PER GRAMME OF SOIL FROM BARNFIELD FARMYARD MANURE PLOT, GROUPED ACCORDING TO THE PERCENTAGE SOIL MOISTURE.

Moisture.	Numbers in Thousands.					
	9-11.	12-14.	15-17.	18-20.	21-23.	24-26.
Nægleria. Total . .	91	63	159	123	129	72
,, Per cent. actives	38·4	47·2	64·6	54·2	44·9	19·7
Heteromita. Total . .	349	301	291	198	201	192
,, Per cent. actives	87·0	63·9	63·1	56·7	60·5	31·8
Oicomonas. Total . .	84	81	123	91	74	87
,, Per cent. actives	44·8	43·6	61·2	53·5	51·1	33·4

p. 15), such a conclusion appears to be justified. In the case of Nægleria the actual total figures in Section I of Table 28 are definitely lower than the expectation ; in

TABLE 28.—AVERAGE DAILY NUMBERS OF TWO SPECIES OF PROTOZOA GIVEN IN THOUSANDS PER GRAMME AT DIFFERENT TEMPERATURES AND MOISTURES.

Temperature in °F.			Totals.		Percentage Actives.	
			Actual.	Expected.	Actual.	Expected.
56-59·9.	I. 9 July. 7 August. 3 October. Moisture 22·0-23·9.	Nægleria	14·8	28·4	39·9	34·7
		Heteromita	99·8	123·9	58·7	53·2
	II. 4 August. 11 September. 1 October. Moisture 18·0-19·9.	Nægleria	24·7	32·7	48·3	47·7
		Heteromita	159·9	157·3	48·7	52·8
42·0-45·9.	III. 22 January. 6 November. 9 December.	Nægleria	245·4	220·7	67·2	59·4
		Heteromita	290·3	285·6	61·3	63·4
	IV. 7 March. 4 April. 1 October. 1 February.	Nægleria	159·7	151·9	66·7	61·9
		Heteromita	246·2	250·4	66·5	62·5

Section III both the actual total number and the percentage of active forms are higher than the expectation, so that the lower temperatures are definitely favourable for this species. The other sections of the Table substantiate this, but the differences are not so marked at the lower moisture content. In Heteromita, although in Section I the total numbers are well below the expectation, the other sections do not support the view that the activity of Heteromita is affected by temperature and moisture. In the soil on which these counts were done the moisture never fell below the limiting value for protozoan development, which laboratory experiments (13) have shown to be 1/6 to 1/5 of the water-holding capacity.

Although it might be expected that rainfall would have an influence on growth and reproduction, yet no connection between the two has been traced (16), but it is possible that data obtained from a very light soil, or under very arid conditions where the amount of water had sunk to an extremely low value, would show a correlation between rainfall and activity.

As a general rule it is customary in laboratory practice to adjust the culture medium to a hydrogen ion concentration of about 7·2, that is to say, approximately to neutrality, when growing protozoa. This may possibly account for the widespread expectation that protozoa will be sensitive to changes in reaction ; but repeated experiments on a variety of species have shown that the great majority can live healthily throughout a very wide range, though within this range there may be an optimum value. Sandon (41) found that the average number of species of flagellates, ciliates, and naked amœbæ were not appreciably different in soils with high or low pH values, from those in neutral soils. In the case of the testaceous rhizopods, however, alkaline soils were unfavourable, while peaty soils, and other acid soils, yielded high numbers. Individual species were not considered in this connection, but only the numbers of species that were found.

Similar results showing the comparative indifference of soil protozoa to extremes of pH value have been obtained by other workers, a case in point being the record of 13,000 common soil flagellates and 160 amœbæ per gramme, most of which were active, from one of the grass plots at Rothamsted having a pH value of 3·65 (41). In cultures the same tolerance is found ; Nasir, in an unpublished experiment, showed that the three soil species *Nægleria gruberi*, *Heteromita globosa*, and *Colpoda cucullus* could grow at a pH value of 9·75, while the lower limit was in each case respectively 3·9, 4·5 and 3·5. Other free-living forms of protozoa, which have been grown extensively in artificial culture media, show the same powers of adaptation. Unfortunately the criticism which is made of all cultural work can be levelled at these experiments ; namely, that cultural conditions do not reproduce natural ones, and that results obtained from cultures should be used with caution in trying to explain the events that occur in nature.

Observations on gravel filters receiving a dilute sugar solution for purification afforded an opportunity of studying the effect of pH values on protozoal distribution under natural conditions ; the filters were divided into sections for convenience of manipulation, and the pH values ranged from 4·3 in the top section to 8·0 at the bottom of the filter, as the sugar in the percolating liquid was changed by bacterial action, firstly to organic acids and ultimately to carbon dioxide and water (15).

In such filters the pH value is not the only condition which may affect the distribution of the protozoa since there are at least four other variables : the degree of purification of the medium, the changing food supply, direct chemical action and, lastly, the presence of large numbers of particular bacteria which may develop in the solution in response to the presence of certain chemical substances. The influence of all these variables can to some extent be eliminated by only dealing with one section of the filter at a time.

Thus, it is manifestly unfair to compare the protozoa found in the top section of the filter, which contains a large percentage of oxidisable material and a large bacterial population, with those in the bottom section where the solution is comparatively pure and the numbers of bacteria very much reduced. A large number of protozoan species were found in the filters, some of them occurring more or less sporadically while others were relatively constant. Of these latter the following six species may be considered in detail : *Colpidium colpoda* Stein, *Paramœcium putrinum* Clap. and Lach., *Pleuronema chrysalis* Ehrbg., *Arcella vulgaris* Ehrbg., *Bodo saltans* Ehrbg., and *Cinetochilum margaritacium* Ehrbg. (Table 29). All of these except Cinetochilum have been recorded from soil.

Although Colpidium can grow successfully throughout the range of pH values that are recorded, it occurs more frequently at the higher values in the top section, though this is not the case in the lower sections ; probably this is due to the fact that it appeared sporadically at the bottom of the filter, only being present 27 per cent. of the possible times, and it may therefore have been a casual contaminant and not a regular member of the population at this level. Paramœcium behaves similarly in that it occurs throughout the range, with a slight falling off at the acid end. Pleuronema is definitely limited by acid conditions since, when the pH value lies above 6·0, the numbers are increased. Arcella occurs very rarely in the upper sections though it is common at the bottom of the filter and, on the whole, it is more successful at the lower pH values. In this respect it conforms to the behaviour of other testaceous rhizopods under field conditions. Bodo is not very common at any level of the filter and its distribution, when correlated with pH values, shows curious irregularities, since it has two maxima, one at an acid value of 5·3 and the other at a slightly alkaline point. It is possible that this peculiarity is due to the presence of different physiological

TABLE 29.—NUMBER OF TIMES SIX SPECIES OCCURRED IN SECTION 1 AND
SECTIONS 5 AND 6 OF SUGAR FILTER AT DIFFERENT pH VALUES,
EXPRESSED AS PERCENTAGES OF THE TOTAL OCCURRENCES.

Range of pH.	Percentage occurrences of Species.					
	Colpidium.	Para-mœcium.	Pleuro-nema.	Arcella.	Bodo.	Cineto-chilum.
	Section 1 of Filter.					
under 4·9	38·9	25·0	0	0	5·5	0
4·9-5·2	50·0	33·3	8·5	33·3	54·5	0
5·3-5·6	68·1	41·8	25·9	15·4	56·0	0
5·7-6·0	67·6	50·0	20·5	9·4	27·6	9·4
6·1-6·4	84·0	61·6	53·3	13·9	43·5	23·5
6·5-6·8	86·1	83·3	77·5	9·7	52·8	27·9
6·9-7·2	90·0	82·7	88·0	14·5	74·4	29·4
over 7·2	72·2	70·6	53·3	0	64·3	—
Total percentage occurrences in Sect. 1.	64·6	67·1	56·1	11·7	39·6	21·6
	Sections 5 and 6 of Filter.					
5·3-5·6	50·0	33·3	0	100·0	33·3	0
5·7-6·0	66·6	100·0	0	100·0	33·3	28·5
6·1-6·4	81·1	28·5	23·9	89·9	28·5	55·8
6·5-6·8	19·7	65·5	23·1	68·4	27·2	70·5
6·9-7·2	48·0	74·4	55·0	71·5	24·8	65·5
over 7·2	37·6	63·3	51·1	69·3	47·6	50·0
Total percentage occurrences in Sects. 5 and 6.	33·0	66·4	43·2	71·8	27·6	67·8

strains, but the evidence is insufficient to establish this
with certainty, although, if the distribution in Section 2
is also considered, the same thing is observed (Table 30).
The extreme case of limitation is shown by Cinetochilum,
where pH values below 6·0 are definitely inimical.

Although such physical factors as temperature, moisture,
and hydrogen ion concentration are not without effect upon
the activity and growth of protozoa, and although the bacteria which are available for their food also help to determine
their numbers, these factors alone are not sufficient to account

TABLE 30.—NUMBER OF TIMES *BODO SALTANS* OCCURRED IN SECTION 2 OF
A SUGAR FILTER AT DIFFERENT *p*H VALUES EXPRESSED AS PERCENT-
AGES OF THE TOTAL OCCURRENCES.

Range of *p*H.	Percentage Occurrence of *Bodo Saltans* in Section 2.
under 4·9	25·0
4·9-5·2	20·0
5·3-5·6	60·0
5·7-6·0	65·8
6·1-6·4	43·5
6·5-6·8	30·6
6·9-7·2	28·8
over 7·2	40·9
Total percentage occurrences in Sect. 2.	27·0

for the changes in numbers that are constantly occurring
in ordinary field soils. If the numbers of any one of the
various species of protozoa are followed from day to day
the changes are amazing and inexplicable (Fig. 16), unless
the hypothesis is accepted that in protoplasm there is
an inherent tendency to periodic reproduction which may
occur at regular or irregular intervals. Thus if it is assumed
that a species has a regular recurring period of increased
reproductive activity, which in the accompanying diagram
(Fig. 17) is arbitrarily assumed to be 41 hours, and that
there is also a more or less steady death-rate, then counts
made at twenty-four hour intervals, or at any other regular
interval of time for that matter, would give a picture
similar to that obtained from actual soil counts. This,
however, is presupposing that no external condition inter-
vened to upset the regularity of the forty-one hourly period
and further, that the peaks attained during the period of maximum reproduction were of about the same height. In the soil
such a regular reproduction would be liable to be hastened
or delayed by a variety of agencies and, therefore, even on
a long series of observations, although fluctuations would be
found, no regularity would be detected.

This explanation of the facts is purely hypothetical,

6 *

but in the case of one species of soil flagellate, *Oicomonas termo*, there is definite evidence of regular periodic increases and decreases of numbers (16). In this form the

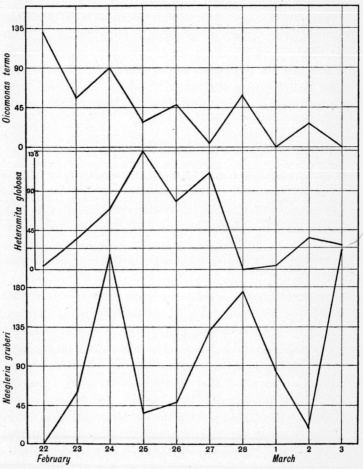

FIG. 16.—Daily variations in the numbers of active forms of three species of protozoa in manured soil on ten successive days in February and March, 1921. The numbers are given in thousands per gramme of soil.

numbers of active organisms rise and fall on alternate days (Fig. 18) with very few exceptions over a long period of time.

It is a matter of opinion whether such a vital rhythm can be invoked to account for the continually changing numbers in all the members of the soil population, but it certainly adds weight to the argument to consider how much the life of every organism depends upon rhythmical processes. Apart from the rhythmical muscular contractions that cause the circulation of the blood and the involuntary movements of the intestine in the higher animals, there are other rhythms whose periodicity is less frequent which, in many cases, have acquired a connection with the sexual life of the

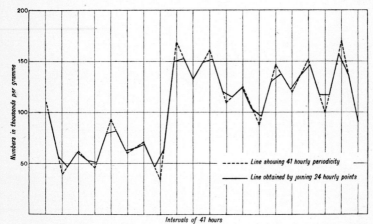

FIG. 17.—Diagram showing what would occur if the numbers of an organism having a 41-hourly reproductive periodicity were counted at 24-hourly intervals.

organism. Examples of these wider rhythms are legion, and can be found in the breeding habits of the majority of animals, while in the malaria parasite the periodic production of sporozoites in the human blood is a regularly recurring event of the same kind though, in this case, it is not sexual in character.

It has already been shown (Fig. 15) that in the soil protozoa there are two periods of maximum growth during the year, one in the late spring and the other in November. This can also be explained on the supposition that it too is due to an inherent urge in the spring and the late autumn which causes an increase in vital activity, and is in this case reflected in an increase in numbers. Among the lower organisms bacteria, protozoa, algæ (47), fungi, and the plankton of the sea (25) all show the same seasonal rhythms, and, to take the other end of the scale, Havelock Ellis (18) draws attention to similar rhythms in human beings. Among his examples such diverse cases are quoted as the fact that there is a distinct rise in bread consumption during the spring

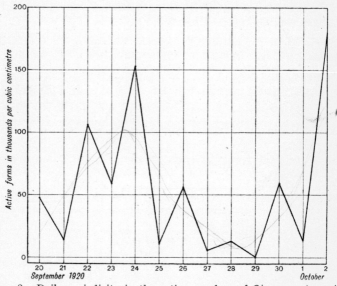

FIG. 18.—Daily periodicity in the active numbers of *Oicomonas termo* in field soil.

and autumn months, not only among school children, but also among prisoners whose conditions are as monotonous as it is possible to find in the human environment. He further shows that the conception rate is highest at these seasons of the year in European countries : " If we begin at September as the lowest point, we find an autumn rise culminating in the lesser maximum of Christmas, followed by a minor depression in January and February. Then comes the great spring rise, culminating in May, and followed after June by a rapid descent to the minimum." A further interesting example is provided by Ellsworth Huntington (26), who shows that, judging by the average daily mark awarded to students in various educational tests in the United States, there is a definite increase in mental activity in April and again in October or November. Huntington himself explains this by the statement that there is a mental optimum when the outdoor temperature is round about 40° ; this may be so, but it is difficult to believe that temperature alone is responsible for the figures that he quotes.

To sum up the position in so far as it applies to the soil micro-organisms : it appears to us that there is in protoplasm an innate capacity to behave rhythmically, but the periods of the rhythm may be of very different lengths, and, moreover, may be superimposed one upon another. In one organism the protoplasm may manifest many different rhythms in different parts of the body according to the needs of the organs which have utilised this property for their successful functioning ; thus there may be one rhythm for the lungs, another for the heart, and a third for the intestine, none of which are of the same periodicity. Yet another rhythm may be found in the generative organs, where ovulation is strictly periodic, and superimposed upon all these rhythms is the regularly recurring period of increased vitality which occurs in the spring and autumn. How these rhythms have arisen in the cells in the past is a matter for speculation, but it seems certain that of all the habits that protoplasm can acquire this rhythmical activity is one of the most readily accepted and made use of by the organism, since it occurs so frequently. For the same reason it must be a valuable adaptation or it would never have passed the careful sieve of natural selection so many times. It seems legitimate to suppose that the majority of soil organisms show periodic outbursts of growth and reproduction, such as are known to occur in Oicomonas and are exactly paralleled in the malarial parasite, and that these organisms no less than man himself, observe the fundamental law that vitality shall be at its maximum in spring and autumn.

Purely speculatively it may be wondered whether, since the numbers of the majority of soil forms ebb and flow in this way, it would be possible for an animal, which has not adopted a rhythmic method of living, to make its home in a population whose whole balance depends upon it. Such a suggestion might account for the rare occurrence of some species, such as *Bodo saltans*, in the soil, but only further experimental work can throw light upon this point.

CHAPTER VII.

THE INTER-ACTIONS BETWEEN THE SOIL ORGANISMS.

IF the species of protozoa are periodically fluctuating in obedience to an inherent reproductive rhythm is there reason to believe that the bacterial species are behaving in the same way? By analogy with other living things this would appear to be a legitimate assumption, but there is also evidence of its truth from experiments with pure cultures, for, both in cultures in liquid media and in soils, fluctuations occur of the same order as those found in untreated soils.

If all the species of bacteria in soil are fluctuating, each with its own rhythm, and if all modifying influences could be excluded, then a series of counts which did not discriminate between the species would show that the numbers remained relatively constant. But since the numbers do not remain constant it is evident that modifying factors must be at work. Although such factors as moisture and temperature acting either alone or in concert seem to have relatively little effect, yet it is possible that they have more than appears, in that the external environment may modify the rhythm in the same way as it does with cyst formation in *Nægleria gruberi*. The orderly course of the rhythm may be upset in any one of four ways: by agencies which hasten or delay reproduction, or by those which hasten or delay death. There is evidence that in the protozoa, when a condition which has inhibited reproduction is removed, an outburst of activity greater than is normal ensues, suggesting that in a line of organisms there is a certain amount of reproductive energy which will have its way sooner or later.

The course of growth in the cultures of Nægleria shown in Figs. 9 and 10 illustrates this point. Here, when the cysts from the control culture and also from the one that had been treated with mycoides extract were transferred into fresh medium, the amount of reproduction was very much greater in the treated culture. The total reproductive rate in the control up to the point of transference was 4·97, while in the treated it was 1·95, but afterwards it was only 1·13 in the control as against 2·71 in the previously treated culture. If the same type of thing also occurs in the case of the bacteria any agency which postpones the reproductive phase will cause an increase in its magnitude. It is at present impossible to say what these agencies may be, but, at any rate in normal untreated soil, the protozoa are probably the chief cause of the untimely death of bacteria. Since the majority of protozoa in the soil depend upon bacteria for their very existence the bond uniting the two groups is a very close one, and it follows that changes in one group, either qualitative or quantitative, must be reflected in the other. But whether such interaction can be detected in field soil by the methods at present available is another question.

There are certain cases in which changes in one group are known to influence another ; for instance, the effect of partial sterilization of soil, which first brought the whole subject of the function of the protozoa in soil into prominence, is a case in point. The idea that any organisms other than bacteria could have an effect upon soil fertility is of comparatively modern origin since it was first put forward by Russell and Hutchinson in 1909 (39). They showed that partial sterilization of certain soils was followed by an increase in the numbers of the bacteria and by the disappearance of the protozoa, and they suggested that the increased fertility displayed by such soils was caused by the increased numbers of bacteria. They attributed the lower numbers of bacteria which were present before treatment to the predatory action of the protozoa which were continually feeding upon them. On this view the essence of partial sterilization is to use methods which destroy the more sensitive group of organisms without too greatly damaging the bacteria.

There is no doubt that the practice of partial sterilization, no matter how it is effected, does induce profound changes in the soil economy, and there may be causes for the rise in the number of bacteria other than the removal of the action of the protozoa, but the suggestion that this is one of the chief causes is substantiated by experiments on other lines. For instance, an experiment was made to simulate what occurs in normal soils and at the same time to eliminate the various interacting agencies by inoculation experiments. A field soil was sterilized by heat and divided into three portions ; to one portion bacteria were added, to the second the same bacteria together with the amœba Nægleria, and to the third the bacteria with the addition of the flagellate Cercomonas (4). Daily bacterial counts on all three portions showed that the amœbæ and the flagellates had an inhibiting effect on the growth of the bacteria. The protozoa were inoculated as cysts and, in the case of Cercomonas, excystation and growth were probably more rapid than in the case of the amœba, which possibly accounts for the fact that the bacterial numbers in this portion of the soil did not at any time exceed 103 millions per gramme. In both the inoculated soils, however, the numbers of bacteria were definitely reduced below those present in the control.

Turning to a well-manured field soil a year's daily counts of protozoa and of bacteria, using the plate technique, showed a definite inverse relationship between the amœbæ and the bacteria. On 70 per cent. of the days Nægleria was the dominant amœba and its numbers rose and fell as the bacteria decreased and increased ; on another 16 per cent. occasions, when the changes in Nægleria were unrelated to the bacteria, a smaller amœba was present in numbers which could have accounted for the bacterial variations. Statistical treatment shows that these numbers are definitely significant (16), and that the fortunes of the two groups are bound up together, the bond being presumably that which links hunter with hunted. Such a result could only be obtained when the majority of the bacteria counted happened to be forms which were readily eaten by the amœbæ, and this might not occur in every soil, or on every plating medium. In any case the amœbæ cannot be invoked to explain the fluctuations in bacterial numbers that still occur in soils from which all protozoa are absent.

Besides the amœbæ in the soil there are also the flagellates, such as *Cercomonas crassicauda* and *Heteromita globosa*, part of whose food-supply is bacterial. These also undoubtedly play a part in causing the fluctuations in bacterial numbers ; but since the increase or decrease of the active forms of both the amœbæ and flagellates in many cases go hand in hand, it is not possible to evaluate with precision how much the depression of the numbers of bacteria is due to the feeding action of the amœbæ and how much to the flagellates. The amœbæ are larger and require a larger food-supply than do the flagellates and therefore their action masks the smaller effect produced by the flagellates.

All the experimental results make it obvious that in an untreated soil, containing the various living organisms, all with their special food requirements, the question of the bacterial supply is an urgent one. Thus, for instance, a single Nægleria, in order to have a reproductive rate of 2·0, would require about 400,000 bacteria (p. 62), and if there were 26,000 of these amœbæ, which during twenty-four hours became 416,000, in order to produce this number the total requirement of bacteria would have been 52,000 million. When the other bacterial-feeding species of protozoa, such as Cercomonas, Heteromita, and the various species of ciliates are also included, this figure becomes very much higher. But it must be remembered that, although such high numbers of bacteria have not been found in soil even by the direct method of counting, yet owing to their rapid rate of division they could be produced, and the numbers counted at any one period simply represent those that have not been consumed by the protozoa.

It is established that the presence of protozoa prevents the bacteria from attaining to as high a level as they would do in a soil devoid of protozoa but, in view of what is known in cultures about individual bacterial efficiency in relation to total numbers, it is by no means so clear that reduction in numbers of necessity causes a corresponding diminution in the amount of chemical work done by the bacteria belonging to the different physiological groups.

Three very common soil processes have been considered from this point of view : nitrogen fixation, carbon dioxide production, and ammonification. It has been found (5, 32) that the presence of protozoa actually increases the amount of nitrogen fixed by *Azotobacter chroococcum*, although their numbers are decreased. This is true not only of cultures in a suitable mannite medium, but it also holds good for soils which had been previously sterilized and reinoculated. The sequence of events in a culture containing protozoa as well as bacteria is very involved. The bacteria will perpetually try to reach the level that the culture medium will support, while the protozoa will steadily reduce their numbers, and a count made at any one moment gives no indication of the numbers of bacteria that have had a transitory existence and added their quota to the work done before vanishing in the bodies of their natural enemies. Therefore if the amount of work done is compared with the numbers of organisms recorded an exaggerated idea of the individual efficiency of the bacteria may be obtained. In the case of nitrogen fixation the nitrogen accumulates in the culture in one form or another, much of it being locked up in the protoplasm of the organisms, and it is not easy to compare the amount fixed in short intervals of time with the changing numbers of the population. In the case of carbon dioxide formation, however, the volume of gas can be estimated very easily without disturbing growth, and can be related with the numbers of bacteria which are producing it (Table 31). The figures in this table show that the efficiency of the bacteria when amœbæ were present is very much

TABLE 31.—AVERAGE EFFICIENCY PER 1000 MILLION BACTERIA AT DIFFERENT BACTERIAL DENSITIES IN THE PRESENCE AND ABSENCE OF AMŒBÆ.

Density of Bacteria in Millions per Cubic Centimetre.	Bacteria + Amœbæ.		Bacteria alone.	
	No. of Cases.	Average Efficiency.	No. of Cases.	Average Efficiency.
0-100	6	0·000732	0	—
100-200	8	0·000156	4	0·000093
200-300	4	0·000134	9	0·000079
300-400	5	0·000106	2	0·000083
400-500	3	0·000101	2	0·000037
500-600	3	0·000062	6	0·000035

exaggerated, which supports the conclusion that a larger population had been present than appears; nevertheless, it is definitely known that the density of the bacterial population is inversely related to individual efficiency (p. 40), and therefore the net tresult of the presence of protozoa is to keep the bacterial numbers nearer to the level of maximum efficiency. In fact, a medium containing protozoa supports many more bacteria whose lives are short, than a medium in which the bacteria are unmolested which supports a smaller number with a greater average span of life.

In the case of ammonification the same sequence of events is found, for in liquid cultures there is an inverse relation between the numbers of bacteria and their efficiency.

The greatest rate of production of ammonia, using "YB" bacteria and a peptone medium, occurred at a bacterial density of about 500 million per cubic centimetre, while any increase in numbers above this level lowered the rate of ammonia production (28, 29).

In sand cultures under similar conditions where Hartmanella was also present, the bacterial numbers were reduced, but the rate of ammonia production increased. The same thing also occurred in cultures of Colpidium with two species of bacteria, both on peptone in a soil extract medium and also on a synthetic medium containing alanine. Here, the same explanation holds good as in the case of carbon dioxide production.

It must be borne in mind that the protozoa and the bacteria are not the only groups of micro-organisms making their homes in the soil, for there are also the fungi, and algæ, which are sufficiently numerous to influence the food-supply of the green plant by their actions on the nitrogen and carbon resources of the soil, and which may, in the same way, indirectly interfere with the course of growth of the bacteria and the protozoa. Since, moreover, both fungi and algæ are used as food by some of the protozoa, they may also have a direct effect on certain species, and there is the further possibility that the fungi, or the products of their growth, are inimical to some of the other organisms. As far as the fungi are concerned there is not very much precise information about their life in the soil. It is extremely difficult to estimate the amount of fungus growth because any method which involves shaking the soil may break pieces of mycelium into numerous fragments, and, after incubation, a plate will show each piece as a separate colony. The chief importance of the fungi from the agricultural point of view is probably as decomposers of celluloses and hemi-celluloses, though they can also act upon a variety of other organic compounds. As far as is known they neither fix nitrogen nor take any part in the formation of nitrites and nitrates, but many fungi are powerful ammonifiers. They can also utilise nitrogen in many different forms, both organic and inorganic, for their own growth. The fungi, on the whole, can live healthily at low pH values, and certain species appear to be ubiquitous; like the bacteria and protozoa it is probable that their numbers fluctuate at short intervals of time, and they exhibit the same seasonal variations.

The algæ in the soil are present either on the surface or distributed through the first few inches, and their locality determines the type of physiological behaviour which they exhibit. By definition algæ are micro-organisms which have the power of producing chlorophyll, and those which are exposed to the light can assimilate carbon dioxide from the air and so add to the stores of carbon which the soil contains, but those which are buried, and in which the chlorophyll cannot function, depend upon organic compounds in solution for their nutriment. The carbon content of a soil is probably the chief factor determining the number of algæ that occur, for there are undoubtedly many more in a soil receiving farmyard manure than there are in a similar unmanured soil. Bristol Roach's work (1) suggests that the numbers in arable soils are lower that those of the amœbæ.

When all the soil inhabitants are considered together the amount of protoplasm in a fertile soil assumes striking proportions. It is impossible to present a census of the complete population of any one soil, for when the numbers fluctuate so much, only an average of numerous observations is of any real value and this is not available in the majority of cases. But some idea of the probable population of a well-manured arable soil can be gleaned from the observations of various workers (Table 32).

In any environment which is not subjected to drastic changes, climatic or otherwise, and provided that the population has not been upset by extensive immigration, a balanced relationship between the various groups of inhabitants is the inevitable result of natural selection. Sudden

TABLE 32.—NUMBERS OF ORGANISMS IN ARABLE SOILS.

Larger Animals : numbers per acre of soil, Broadbalk dunged plot.

Nematodes	. . .	3,609,000	Morris
Myriapods	. . .	1,781,000	,,
Insects	. . . .	7,727,000	,,
Earthworms	. . .	1,010,000	,,

Protozoa : numbers per gramme of soil (average of 365 days), Barnfield dunged plot.

Nægleria	. . . .	131,000	Cutler, Crump and Sandon
Heteromita	. . .	240,000	,, ,,
Oicomonas	. . .	101,700	,, ,,
Cercomonas	. . .	4,621	,, ,,

Plants : numbers per gramme of soil, Broadbalk dunged plot.

Green algæ	. . .	39,560 (average 6 samples)	Bristol Roach
Fungi	. . . .	775,000 (average 14 samples)	Russell

Bacteria : millions per gramme of soil, Barnfield dunged plot. .

Total numbers, plating method	.	27·7 (average 365 days)	Cutler, Crump and Sandon

changes in the environment, or its invasion by new species may disturb the balance that has been so laboriously achieved ; but, even so, it will eventually be restored by the adaptation of the existing population to the new environment, or, where it is a case of invasion, by the annihilation of the disturbing factor, or by its amalgamation with the colonists already established there. This is as true of the soil as it is of all other natural environments.

As might be expected any agency that upsets the community that has arrived at such a state of equilibrium with its surroundings will produce effects out of all proportion to the original cause. There are numerous instances of such disturbances of a natural balance, for example, as a straightforward case, the well-known effects of the introduction of rabbits into Australia and New Zealand may be cited ; but a case involving more ramifications is quoted by Elton (19) and serves to illustrate the intricate relationships that exist between different groups in the same area. " Some keen gardener, intent upon making Hawaii even more beautiful than before, introduced a plant called *Lantana camara*, which in its native home of Mexico causes no trouble to anybody.   Meanwhile, someone else had also improved the amenities of the place by introducing turtle-doves from China, which, unlike any of the native birds, fed eagerly upon the berries of Lantana.   The combined effects of the vegetative powers of the plant and the spreading of seeds by the turtle-doves were to make the Lantana multiply exceedingly and become a serious pest on the grazing country. Indian mynah birds were also introduced, and they too fed upon Lantana berries.   After a few years the birds of both species had increased enormously in numbers.   But there is another side to the story.   Formerly the grasslands and young sugar-cane plantations had been ravaged yearly by vast numbers of army-worm caterpillars, but the mynahs also fed upon these caterpillars and succeeded to a large extent in keeping them in check, so that the outbreaks became less severe.   About this time certain insects were introduced in order to try and check the spread of Lantana, and several of these (in particular a species of Agronomyzid fly) did actually destroy so much seed that the Lantana began to decrease.   As a result of this, the mynahs also began to decrease in numbers to such an extent that there began to occur again severe outbreaks of army-worm caterpillars.   It was then found that when the Lantana had been removed in many places, other introduced shrubs came in, some of which are even more difficult to eradicate than the original Lantana."

The traditional methods of agriculture used in the past, and which have been handed down from father to son, improved the soil and added to its store of food for both plants and micro-organisms without materially altering the balance of the population.   But a new era in agriculture has been ushered in by the introduction of artificial fertilisers, by new methods of cultivation, and by the overthrow of the old cropping system and more intensive crop production.   This has placed the balance in jeopardy, and has made it more and more necessary to increase the sum total of knowledge, not only of soil conditions but also of the soil inhabitants and their reactions. It seems probable that the safeguarding of the balanced condition of the soil is one of the duties of the new generation of agriculturists, and this can only be attained by increased knowledge linked with its application to practice in the field.

LIST OF LITERATURE CITED.

1. Bristol Roach, B. M. (1927), "On the algæ of some normal English soils." *J. Agric. Sci.*, **17**, 563-588.

2. Conn, H. J. (1918), "The microscopic study of bacteria and fungi in soils." *N.Y. Agric. Expt. Sta. Bull.*, No. 64.

3. Cutler, D. W. (1920), "A method for estimating the number of active protozoa in the soil." *J. Agric. Sci.*, **9**, 135-143.

4. Cutler, D. W. (1923), "The action of protozoa on bacteria when inoculated into sterile soil." *Ann. App. Biol.*, **10**, 137-141.

5. Cutler, D. W. and Bal, D. V. (1926), "Influence of protozoa on the process of nitrogen fixation by *Azotobacter chroococcum*." *Ann. App. Biol.*, **18**, 516-534.

6. Cutler, D. W. and Crump, L. M. (1923), "The rate of reproduction in artificial culture of *Colpidium colpoda*." *Biochem. J.*, **17**, 174-186.

7. Cutler, D. W. and Crump, L. M. (1923), "The rate of reproduction in artificial culture of *Colpidium colpoda*." Part II., *Biochem. J.*, **17**, 878-886.

8. Cutler, D. W. and Crump, L. M. (1924), "The rate of reproduction in artificial culture of *Colpidium colpoda*." Part III., *Biochem. J.*, **18**, 905-912.

9. Cutler, D. W. and Crump, L. M. (1927), "The qualitative and quantitative effects of food on the growth of a soil amœba (*Hartmanella hyalina*)." *Brit. J. Exper. Biol.*, **5**, 155-165.

10. Cutler, D. W. and Crump, L. M. (1929), "Carbon dioxide production in sands and soils in the presence and absence of amœbæ." *Ann. App. Biol.*, **16**, 472-482.

11. Cutler, D. W. and Crump, L. M. (1933), "Some aspects of the physiology of certain nitrite-forming bacteria." *Ann. App. Biol.*, **20**, 291-296.

12. Cutler, D. W. and Crump, L. M. (1935), "The effect of bacterial products on amœbic growth." *Brit. J. Exper. Biol.*, **12**, 52-58.

13. Cutler, D. W. and Dixon, A. (1927), "The effect of soil storage and water content on the protozoan population." *Ann. App. Biol.*, **17**, 247-254.

14. Cutler, D. W. and Mukerji, B. K. (1931), "Nitrite formation by soil bacteria, other than Nitrosomonas." *Proc. Roy. Soc. B.*, **108**, 384-394.

15. Cutler, D. W., Crump, L. M. and Dixon A. (1932), "Some factors influencing the distribution of certain protozoa in biological filters." *J. Animal Ecology*, **1**, 143-151.

16. Cutler, D. W., Crump, L. M. and Sandon, H. (1922), " A quantitative investigation of the bacterial and protozoan population of the soil, with an account of the protozoan fauna." *Phil. Trans. Roy. Soc. B.*, **211**, 317-350.

17. Darwin, C. (1881), "Vegetable mould and earthworms." John Murray, London.

18. Ellis, H. (1910), "Studies in the Psychology of Sex." Vol. I. Philadelphia: F. A. Davis Company.

19. Elton, C. (1927), "Animal Ecology." London: Sidgwick & Jackson, Ltd.

20. Fisher, R. A. (1934), " Statistical methods for research workers." Oliver & Boyd, Edinburgh.

21. Frankland, P. F. and Frankland, G. C. (1890), " The nitrifying process and its specific ferment." *Phil. Trans. Roy. Soc. B.*, **181**, 107-128.

22. Fremlin, H. S. (1903), " On the cultivation of the Nitrosobacterium." *J. of Hygiene*, **3**, 364-379.

23. Fremlin, H. S. (1914), " Further observations on Nitrosobacteria." *J. of Hygiene*, **14**, 149-162.

24. Fremlin, H. S. (1930), " Further notes on the culture of Nitrosobacterium." *J. of Hygiene*, **29**, 236-242.

25. Herdman, W. A. (1922), " Spolia Runiana V." *J. Linn. Soc.* (*Botany*), **46.**

26. Huntington, E., Williams, F. E. and v. Valkenburg, S. (1933), "Economic and Social Geography." New York: John Wiley & Sons, Inc.

27. Maltaux, M. and Massart, J. (1906), " Sur les excitants de la division cellulaire." *Rec. d. l'Inst. Bot. d. Brux.*, **6.**

28. Meiklejohn, J. (1930), " The relation between the numbers of a soil bacterium and the ammonia produced by it in peptone solutions ; with some reference to the effect on this process of the presence of amœbæ." *Ann. App. Biol.*, **17**, 614-637.

29. Meiklejohn, J. (1932), " The effect of Colpidium on ammonia production by soil bacteria." *Ann. App. Biol.*, **19**, 584-608.

30. Morris, H. M. (1922), " The insect and other invertebrate fauna of arable land at Rothamsted." *Ann. App. Biol.*, **9**, 282-305.

31. Müller, A. (1873), "Über den gegenwärtigen Stand der Städte reinigungs—und Wasserbeschaffungsfrage für Berlin." Land. Versuchs-Stat., **16**, 241-273.

32. Nasir, S. A. (1923), " Some preliminary investigations on the relationship of protozoa to soil fertility, with special reference to nitrogen fixation." *Ann. App. Biol.*, **10**, 122-133.

33. Oehler, R. (1916), "Amöbenzucht auf reinem Boden." *Arch. f. Protistenk.*, **37**, 175-190.

34. Peskett, G. L. (1924), " Allelocatalysis and the growth of yeast." *Biochem. J.*, **18**, 866-871.

35. Peskett, G. L. (1933), " Growth factors of lower organisms." *Biol. Rev.*, **8**, 1-45.

36. Robertson, T. B. (1924), " Principles of Biochemistry." London: Baillière, Tindall & Cox.

37. Russell, E. J. (1932), " Soil conditions and plant growth." (Rothamsted Monographs on Agricultural Science Series.) Longmans, Green & Co., London.

38. Russell, E. J. and Appleyard, A. (1915), " The atmosphere of the soil: its composition and the causes of variation." *J. Agric. Sci.*, **7**, 1-48.

39. Russell, E. J. and Hutchinson, H. B. (1909), " The effect of partial sterilization of soil on the production of plant food." *J. Agric. Sci.*, **3**, 111-144.

40. Sack, J. (1925), " Eine nitritbildende Bakterie." *Centralbl. f. Bakt. Abt. II.*, **64**, 32-37.

41. Sandon, H. (1927), " The composition and distribution of the protozoan fauna of the soil." Oliver & Boyd, Edinburgh.

42. Schloesing, Th. and Müntz, A. (1877), " Sur la nitrification par les ferments organisés," *Compt. rend.*, **84**, 301-303.

43. Severtzova, L. B. (1928), " Food requirements of soil amœbæ with reference to their inter-relation with soil bacteria and soil fungi." *Centralbl. f. Bakt. Abt. II.*, **73**, 162-179.

44. Telegdy-Kovats, L. de (1932), " The growth and respiration of bacteria in sand cultures in the presence and absence of protozoa," *Ann. App. Biol.*, **19**, 65-86.

45. Thornton, H. G. and Gray, P. H. H. (1934), " The numbers of bacterial cells in field soils, as estimated by the ratio method," *Proc. Roy. Soc. B.*, **115**, 522-543.

46. Warington, R. (1878), " On nitrification," Part I., *J. Chem. Soc.*, **33**, 44-51 ; (1879), Part II., *ibid.*, **35**, 429-456 ; (1884), Part III., *ibid.*, **45**, 637-672 ; (1891), Part IV., *ibid.*, **59**, 484-529.

47. West, W. and West, G. S. (1912), " On the periodicity of the phytoplankton of some British lakes," *J. Linn. Soc. (Botany)*, **40.**

48. Winogradsky, S. (1890), " Recherches sur les organismes de nitrification," *Ann. de. l'Inst. Pasteur*, **4**, 213-231.

49. Winogradsky, S. (1892), " Contributions à la morphologie des organismes de la nitrification," *Arch. d. Sci. Biol.*, **1**, 87-137.

50. Woodruff, L. L. and Baitsell, G. A. (1911), " The temperature coefficient of the rate of reproduction of *Paramœcium aurelia*," *Amer. J. Phys.*, **29**, 147-155.

INDEX.

PRINTED IN GREAT BRITAIN BY THE UNIVERSITY PRESS, ABERDEEN

am